the mystery of the
expanding universe

WILLIAM BONNOR

The Mystery of THE

EXPANDING

UNIVERSE

1964

MACMILLAN PUBLISHING CO., INC.
NEW YORK

COLLIER MACMILLAN PUBLISHERS
LONDON

FIFTH PRINTING 1973

Macmillan Publishing Co., Inc.
866 Third Avenue
New York, N.Y. 10022

Collier-Macmillan Canada Ltd., Toronto, Ontario

Library of Congress catalog card number: 63–14542

Printed in the United States of America

preface

This book is intended for the intelligent person who wants to know what modern cosmology is about. It assumes no previous knowledge of the subject and no mathematics, though there are a few footnotes for readers with a mathematical turn of mind. The physics and astronomy required are supplied as the need arises.

I am grateful to Dr. W. Davidson, Miss M. Dixon, Mr. J. Kershaw, and Dr. G. Stephenson for their criticism of the original manuscript.

WILLIAM BONNOR

London,
July 26, 1963

contents

plates

(following page 20)

figures

I

introduction

Until this century, astronomers thought that the universe was essentially static. Although they knew that the stars had local movements, they believed that the average motion of the whole was nil. The universe of stars seemed to form an immutable background to terrestrial change and motion.

The discoveries that destroyed this picture form one of the most important scientific and philosophical revolutions of our time. The first step was taken by V. M. Slipher of the Lowell Observatory, who in 1912 found that the great Andromeda galaxy had a speed of 125 miles per second. By 1917 Slipher had measured the speeds of several nearby galaxies, and found them all in rapid motion. Since the movement was in nearly all cases one of recession from the solar system, it seemed unlikely that the motions were random.

At the same time another scientific revolution was taking place, for Einstein had just put forward his general theory of relativity. This is a theory of gravitation, and as such was designed to deal with terrestrial physics and the astronomy of the solar system; but it was soon found to have far-reaching cosmological implications, and in 1917 an investigation by Willem de Sitter, based on general relativity, suggested that the universe might be in a process of overall expansion.

More than ten years passed before the observations of the American astronomer Edwin Hubble established beyond reasonable doubt that the universe was expanding. The old conception of a static universe was overthrown, and scientists and philosophers were challenged with questions such as "What started the expansion?" and "Has the universe a beginning and an end?"

The 1930's were a period of intense activity in theoretical cosmology. The implications of general relativity were worked out in much detail, and it was found that the theory offered many universes of very different properties and histories, all consistent with the meager observed data. Since then, theoretical cosmologists have been waiting, with varying degrees of patience, for observations which would decide between the many possibilities.

General relativity has not been the only theory used in cosmology. In 1935 E. A. Milne of Oxford put forward, as a basis for a cosmological theory, what he called kinematic relativity. Although it attracted much attention at first, Milne's theory is now largely neglected. The reason probably is that although Milne produced a satisfactory model of the universe, his work, unlike the cosmology of Einstein's relativity, was not supported by an adequate theory of gravitation.

Recently, another rival to relativistic cosmology has appeared—the steady-state theory of Hermann Bondi, Thomas Gold, and Fred Hoyle. According to this, although the galaxies recede from one another, the large-scale picture of the universe does not change. To maintain this stationary condition, it is necessary for matter to be spontaneously created in empty space, out of nothing.

Philosophically, the steady-state model is of great interest. In the first place, it is extremely simple. Second, questions about the start and finish of the expansion do not arise because the universe has always been expanding, and will continue to do so forever. Third—and this is a point on which Bondi in particular lays great stress—since the universe on a large scale is much the same at all times and places, we can have great confidence in extrapolating the laws of physics as we know them to other parts of the universe, and to other periods in its history. Such confidence is not justified, Bondi argues, in dealing with models of the universe which change drastically with time.

The steady-state theory has aroused great controversy, some of it forthright to the point of rudeness, though the authors have defended their position with patience and restraint. I shall try to present honestly the various aspects of the controversy, but I must warn the reader at once that, from the scientific and mathematical points of view, I do not think very much of the steady-state theory, and I expect its rivalry to relativistic cosmology to be as short-lived as that of Milne's theory.

The book is divided into four parts. In Part I I give an idea of the scale of size we use in cosmology, and describe the properties of stars and galaxies which are needed later. In Part II I present a description of the observations a successful cosmological theory must account for. Cosmology is one of the branches of physics in which theory is well ahead of observation. By this I mean that theorists can explain all the known facts, and are panting for more observed data to help them settle their disputes. This is the opposite of the situation in, for example, the physics of elementary particles, where there are plenty of experimental results and little adequate theory. It tends to make theoretical cosmologists somewhat impatient with the observers. I am a theorist, and I find it necessary to remind myself every so often how difficult it is to make reliable observations in cosmology. If I did not do this, I might feel tempted to complain that we have today only slightly more confidence in the observations than we had in Hubble's heyday, a quarter of a century ago; and that the most important observational knowledge to accrue in this period was the detection of a gigantic mistake that observers had been making for many years. (If it had not been for this mistake, described in Chapter 4, the steady-state theory would probably never have been put forward.) And all this in spite of the fact that the famous 200-inch telescope has now been in use for fifteen years.

The reasons why progress in observational cosmology has been very slow should become clear in Part II, where I describe the precarious processes by which the enormous distances between galaxies have to be estimated.

I turn to theoretical cosmology in Part III, and it is here that I make a detailed comparison between the relativistic and the steady-state theories. In Part IV I return to observation, and describe the latest work. There is no doubt that the present state of the observations is very exciting, and there seems at last a good prospect that we shall soon have a definite decision between the two theories. The sifting of the evidence forms Part IV, except for a final summarizing chapter.

the scale of
the universe

the earth, the sun, and the stars

THE SUN AND THE PLANETS

The Earth is one of nine planets held in orbit by the Sun's gravitational field. The Earth goes round the Sun once in 365¼ days, which we call a year. The other planets take longer or shorter times to orbit; for example, Mercury, the one nearest the Sun, takes only 88 days, whereas the most distant, Pluto, takes 248 *years*.

The orbits of all nine planets are roughly circular, with the Sun at the center. The average speeds vary from about 30 miles per second for Mercury to 3 miles per second for

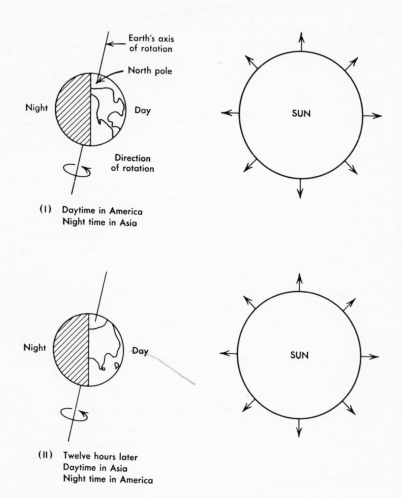

Figure 1. THE SUCCESSION OF NIGHT AND DAY. In Figure 1(i) it is day-time in the Western Hemisphere, because this is lit by the Sun's rays; the Eastern Hemisphere is in shadow. In Figure 1(ii) it is twelve hours later, so the Earth has rotated half of one complete turn; there is now day in the Eastern and night in the Western Hemisphere.

Pluto. The orbital speed of the Earth is 18½ miles per second, or about 66,000 miles per hour.

As well as moving in their orbits, the planets rotate about axes within themselves. In the Earth this axis joins the north and south poles, and one complete revolution takes 24 hours. It is this rotation (and *not* the orbital motion) which is responsible for the regular succession of night and day. As the Earth rotates, a particular place, such as New York, is exposed to the Sun's rays for half the 24 hours (approximately) and is in shadow for the other half (see Figure 1).

The planets have no source of light of their own but reflect the Sun's light, and this is why we see them. The Moon, too, is seen only by the light it reflects from the Sun, and the Earth would be seen from another planet by the Sun's reflected light.

The distances of the planets from the Sun are very large by ordinary standards. The distance of the Sun from the Earth is 93,000,000 miles; from Mercury it is 36,000,000 miles; and from Pluto, about 3,700,000,000 miles. Some idea of what these distances mean can be gained from the fact that a spaceship orbiting the Earth every 90 minutes just above the atmosphere would take six months to cover a distance equal to that between the Earth and the Sun.

The Sun, the nine planets, and various minor planets, comets, and satellites, all of which orbit the Sun, make up the *solar system*. Most of the objects in it, except comets, lie nearly in a plane through the Sun. The distance between the Sun and Pluto gives a rough figure for the extent of the system—it is a circular disc about 3,700,000,000 miles in radius. The solar system is a good deal larger than this, however, if the long cigar-shaped orbits of the comets are taken into account.

LIGHT-SECONDS AND LIGHT-YEARS

The solar system is a tiny island of matter in a vast sea of empty space. Just how vast it is can be gathered from the fact that the nearest star, called Proxima Centauri, is a little less than 30,000,000,000,000 miles from the Sun.

Evidently it would get very tedious if we had to write out a number like this every time we gave a distance. Astronomers use two methods to get over the difficulty.

The first method is to write the above number as 3×10^{13}—which simply means 3 followed by 13 zeroes. Using this system we can write

$$\text{Distance of Sun from Earth} = 93 \times 10^6 \text{ miles *}$$
$$\text{Distance of Sun from Pluto} = 37 \times 10^8 \text{ miles *}$$

This method can be used for any large number, whether it represents a distance or not.

The second method is only for distances, and makes use of the speed of light. Light consists of waves of energy traveling very fast—at 186,000 miles per second. We can express this by saying that 186,000 miles is one light-second, or that the light-time of this distance is one second. Evidently 372,000 miles is two light-seconds, and so on. In this way we can express a distance as a light-time: that is, the time taken by light in traveling it. The formula for the light-time is simply:

$$\text{Distance in miles} \div 186{,}000 = \text{light-time in seconds.}$$

This reduces big distances to manageable numbers. For example, the distance between the Earth and the Sun is

$$93{,}000{,}000 \div 186{,}000 = 500 \text{ light-seconds.}$$

* These are also written 9.3×10^7 and 3.7×10^9.

Since 500 seconds is $8\frac{1}{3}$ minutes, we can also say that the Earth is $8\frac{1}{3}$ light-minutes from the Sun. Still greater distances are expressed in terms of light-hours, light-days, and light-years. Thus, the distance between the Sun and the star Proxima Centauri is somewhat less than 5 light-years. Most of the distances given in this book are expressed in light-years.

In the Table the distances of various celestial bodies are given in miles and in terms of light-time:

TABLE

BODIES	DISTANCE IN MILES	APPROXIMATE LIGHT-TIME
Earth–Moon	239,000	1 second
Earth–Sun	93,000,000	$8\frac{1}{3}$ minutes
Pluto–Sun	37×10^8	$5\frac{1}{2}$ hours
Proxima Centauri–Sun	3×10^{13}	5 years

We see that the distances which cover the solar system, great as they seem compared with terrestrial measurements, are minute when we consider interstellar distances. They will seem even smaller when we come to think of the Milky Way as a whole.

WHAT IS THE SUN?

Almost all the energy we use on Earth has its origin in the Sun, and the continual outpouring of energy as light and heat is the Sun's most remarkable feature.

From the study of fossils we know that there has been life on the Earth's surface for 3,000 million years. We infer that the Sun has been radiating energy at the same rate for this period of time, because otherwise there would have been changes in terrestrial temperatures which would have made life impossible. The actual rate at which energy is poured out is not very large, considering how big the Sun is; one pound of high explosive produces much more energy than one pound of the Sun, but only while the explosion lasts. The amazing thing is that the Sun has been radiating for this enormous length of time without losing its brilliance.

We now know that the Sun's energy comes from a process like the one occurring in a hydrogen bomb. Before explaining this, I shall give a brief summary of the relevant theory of the atom. This will be useful later as well.

Atoms have two parts—a central *nucleus* which contains nearly all the mass, and one or more *electrons* orbiting the nucleus. The nucleus has a positive electric charge which is equal and opposite to the total negative charge of the electrons. When atoms react chemically, the orbits of some electrons get distorted, but the nuclei are unaffected. For example, when hydrogen and oxygen join to form water, some electrons are shared between the atoms of the two elements, although the nuclei are unaltered.

Atomic nuclei can change, however—for instance, in radio-activity. Here a nucleus of, say, uranium just disintegrates spontaneously, giving out radiation and ending up as lead. This type of process is called *nuclear fission,* and is what happens in atomic bombs (as distinct from hydrogen bombs). The radiation given out in the process represents an energy release, and it is this that causes the destruction.

Another process that atomic nuclei undergo is *fusion.* If hydrogen atoms are heated to very high temperatures (millions of degrees), their nuclei can stick together to form a nucleus of helium, which is the next heavier element. In this fusion process energy is given out. This is what happens in a hydrogen bomb. Because high temperatures are essential, it is called a thermonuclear reaction.

This also happens in the Sun, and the energy that the Sun has been pouring out for thousands of millions of years comes from this fusion of hydrogen into helium. Even so, more than half its weight is still hydrogen.

The Sun is almost entirely hydrogen and helium but has traces of other elements which have been formed by more complicated nuclear processes. From our point of view, the most important of these "heavy elements" (so called because they are heavier than helium) are calcium and sodium. These can readily be detected because they affect the light we receive from the Sun, or what is called the Sun's *spectrum*.

Owing to the enormous temperatures, all the elements in the Sun are gaseous. The Sun is thus a huge ball of gas giving out energy because of the thermonuclear transmutation of hydrogen into helium. Fortunately for us the Sun's emission of energy is a self-regulating process which is not likely to vary appreciably during the next few thousand million years.

THE STARS

The Sun is an ordinary star. Stars are all gaseous, and the conversion of hydrogen into helium is going on in all of them; nevertheless they show a great deal of variation. For instance, the temperature at their surfaces can vary from 3,000 to 80,000 degrees centigrade.

Roughly speaking, the hotter the star, the brighter it is. Astrophysicists have classified stars into types of decreasing temperature as follows: O, B, A, F, G, K, M, R, N, S. The mnemonic for this is "Oh! Be a fine girl, kiss me right now, smack." The Sun is type G. Some stars, exceptional because of their size, do not fit into the classification. For instance, there are giant stars which are not very hot but which are bright because of their size, and dwarf stars which are hot but not very bright.

One may ask: Are there any stars which have burned up all their hydrogen? The answer is that we suppose there may be, but because they no longer emit light, we cannot see them. Because some stars are known to be living prodigally, that is, burning up their hydrogen at a very high rate, possibly many have already burned out. We have no hope of observing such stars, which is unfortunate because, as we shall see later, nonluminous matter can play an important part in cosmology.

Finally, just to give an idea of the size of the stars, here are the relevant figures for the Sun. The radius of the Sun is 430,000 miles—about 100 times that of the Earth. Its mass is two billion billion billion* tons, or 2×10^{33} grams,* and that of the Earth is 6×10^{27} grams. Although the Sun is so massive, its average density (mass divided by volume) is only slightly greater than that of water, and only one-quarter the average density of the Earth.

---

* In this book a billion means 1,000 million. I shall sometimes express quantities in the metric system, particularly in grams and centimeters. There are 454 grams in one pound, and 30 centimeters in one foot.

3

the galaxies

THE MILKY WAY

All the stars which can be seen with the naked eye (about 6,000) belong to our galaxy, called the Milky Way, or simply, the Galaxy. The Milky Way contains about a 100 billion stars. It is a disc, like a wheel with a hub at the center. (See Figure 2.) We cannot, of course, see the Milky Way from outside, but it probably looks rather like the galaxy shown in Plate 1. The diameter of the disc is about 100,000 light-years, and the thickness at the center is about 16,000 light-years. This means, of course, that a ray of light would take 100,000 years to travel across the disc, and if we remember that light travels at 186,000 miles per second we get some idea of the gigantic scale of the Galaxy.

To use the phrase of William Herschel, the eighteenth-century British astronomer, the Milky Way is an "island uni-verse." It was Herschel who made the first systematic obser-vations of it and who recognized its unity as a celestial object. Herschel, by the way, exemplifies one of the great virtues of a successful astronomer—patience. Because he was too poor to buy a telescope, he made his own, but only after two hundred failures!

One of the problems that interested Herschel was to find the position of the Sun in the Milky Way. He concluded that it was near the center of the disc. The same conclusion was later reached by the Dutch astronomer J. C. Kapteyn, who at the beginning of this century spent twelve years on the Herculean task of measuring and recording the positions and brightnesses of nearly half a million stars.

In Chapter 4 we shall see how astronomers measure the enormous distances involved in cosmology. In Kapteyn's time, measurements of distance were even harder to make than they are now, and this was one of the reasons why his conclusion was wrong. According to present ideas, the Sun is 30,000 light-years from the center of the Milky Way, as illustrated in Figure 2.

The Milky Way is rotating about an axis through the center at right angles to the disc. This has been found by studying the motion of the Sun relative to other stars. A complete revolution takes 200 million years; nevertheless, owing to its enormous radius the speeds of the stars far from the center are very large. Thus the Sun has a speed of about 140 miles per second about the center of the Milky Way.

Of course, the Earth and the other planets are carried along with the Sun in this rotatory motion. It is worth paus-

Figure 2. THE MILKY WAY SEEN EDGE ON. The Sun is about halfway between the center and the edge.

Sun

ing to think in how many ways you are moving at this moment. First, the Earth is rotating about its own axis, so unless you happen to be at the North or South Pole you are moving in a circle because of this. Second, the Earth is moving in a near circle about the Sun, so you are experiencing this motion too; and third, you are being dragged about the center of the Milky Way. It will become clear later that, fourth, the Milky Way itself is moving with respect to other galaxies. The point of this digression is to show how hard it is to say who or what is "really" motionless. Newton founded his theories on the hypothesis that this is possible, but no one has ever been able to describe how to do it. Einstein said that it was not possible, and this impossibility he made the basis of the theory of relativity. We shall come back to this question in Chapter 7.

OTHER GALAXIES*

William Herschel observed not only the stars of the Milky Way but also certain faint, diffuse patches of light which he conjectured did not belong to the Milky Way at all. His telescope showed that some of these patches really consist of stars, and in 1785 he made the momentous suggestion that they were collections of stars like the Milky Way—other island universes, in fact.

In 1783 the French astronomer Charles Messier had cataloged 103 such objects. Some of these were later found to be nebulae within the Milky Way, but many still bear the numbers Messier gave them: for example, the famous Andromeda galaxy is called M31. (See Plate 11.)

---

* Some cosmologists still use the term "nebula," or "extragalactic nebula," for a large collection of stars, such as the Milky Way, which I call a galaxy. The term "nebula" is also used to denote various clouds of gas and dust which appear inside galaxies. To avoid confusion, it seems to me better to reserve the term "nebula" solely for this latter purpose.

Nowadays the number of galaxies that could be seen though our telescopes, if we had time to look at them all, is estimated to be over ten billion. This has been made possible partly by the building of bigger telescopes, but mainly by the introduction of photography, which enables exposures of faint galaxies to be made for several hours.

Modern detailed observations of galaxies began with Edwin Hubble at Mount Wilson. In 1924 he was able to prove Herschel's guess that some at least of the faint luminous patches are outside the Milky Way. This he did by establishing their distances, which turned out to be enormous, even compared with the dimensions of the Milky Way. Until his death in 1953 Hubble worked ceaselessly to understand the universe of galaxies.

Galaxies show great variety of shape. Hubble's classification, which we still use, is as follows:

1. Irregular galaxies. These have no special geometrical form. Examples are the Magellanic Clouds (Plates 2 and 3) which, 150,000 light-years from the Earth, are the nearest neighbors of our own Galaxy.
2. Regular galaxies. These have a definite central nucleus, and mostly seem to be rotating. They are split into two subclasses:
   a. ellipticals, which are compact with elliptical shape (see Plate 4);
   b. spirals, which are the commonest of all galaxies (see Plates 5, 11, 12).

The Milky Way is a regular galaxy. Much work has been required to find out whether it is an elliptical or a spiral, but at last it seems certain that it is a spiral and that the Sun is in one of the arms.

It is believed that stars are being formed now in the spiral arms of our own and other galaxies, by condensation from gas and dust, which are rather plentiful in the spiral arms. Hydrogen is present there to the extent of one atom per cubic centimeter, which counts as plentiful in galactic space.

The young stars in the arms are brighter than the older ones in the center of the spiral or in elliptical galaxies. Indeed, the difference between the two types is so great that Walter Baade, the famous astronomer of Mount Palomar who died in 1960, asserted that they should be called Population I and Population II respectively. (See Plate 6.)

CLUSTERS OF GALAXIES

The Milky Way is one of a small cluster of galaxies called the Local Group, which includes all galaxies within about two million light-years from the Earth, and contains about twenty members. Beyond this distance one would have to travel about ten million light-years before coming across another galaxy.

Other galaxies, too, show a distinct tendency to cluster. The clusters may be small, like the Local Group, or may contain several hundreds, or even thousands, of galaxies.

One may well ask whether clusters of galaxies are the last in the hierarchy. As stars aggregate into galaxies, and galaxies into clusters, do clusters aggregate into superclusters, and so on? Although astronomers are not quite unanimous, it seems that clusters are the largest individual entities, and we should not be justified in speaking of clusters of clusters.

Thus we have at last reached the unit of cosmology—the cluster of galaxies. In practice the galaxy is usually taken as the unit because galaxies can be recognized more easily than clusters. From now on, our picture of the universe will be a vast number—possibly an infinite number—of galaxies.

I. A SPIRAL GALAXY SEEN EDGE ON. The Milky Way is thought to be similar to this galaxy. The very bright, randomly distributed stars are foreground stars belonging to the Milky Way.

2. THE LESSER MAGELLANIC CLOUD. This and the Greater Magellanic Cloud (Plate 3) are the nearest neighbors of the Milky Way. They are called irregular galaxies, because of their shape.

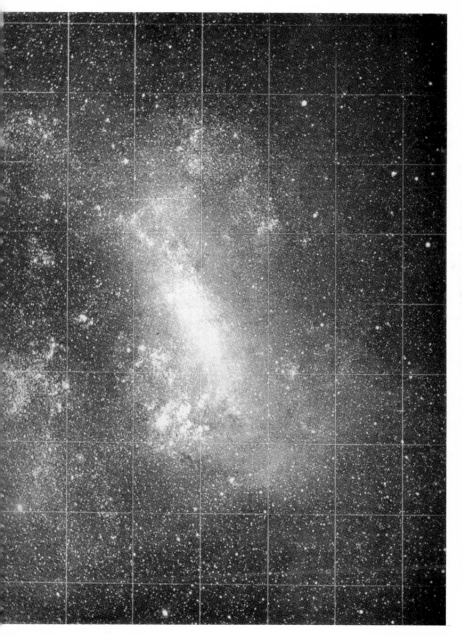

3. THE GREATER MAGELLANIC CLOUD. See caption to Plate 2.

4. ELLIPTICAL GALAXY. This galaxy seems to consist of stars only, and does not show the clouds of gas and dust so conspicuous in spiral galaxies.

5. A BARRED SPIRAL GALAXY. A bar of stars can be seen crossing the central nucleus and meeting the spiral arms.

7. A SPIRAL GALAXY WITH AN ABSORPTION BAND. The Milky Way has a similar absorbing layer that makes it difficult to see along the plane of the disc.

6. STELLAR POPULATIONS I AND II. Andromeda galaxy (top picture) shows giant and supergiant stars of Population I in the spiral arms. The hazy patch at the upper right is composed of unresolved Population II stars. In the lower picture, NGC 205, companion of the Andromeda galaxy, shows stars of Population II. The brightest stars are red, and are 100 times fainter than the blue giants of Population I. The two main pictures show details of the regions indicated in the small side photograph (which is a reduced version of Plate 11).

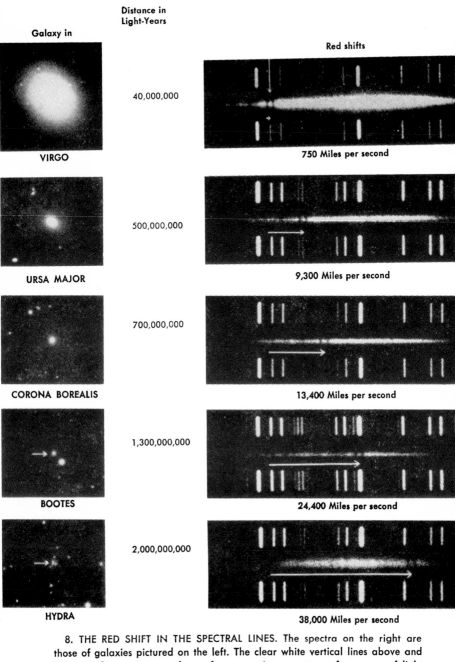

Galaxy in	Distance in Light-Years	Red shifts

Galaxy in

Distance in Light-Years

Red shifts

VIRGO — 40,000,000 — 750 Miles per second

URSA MAJOR — 500,000,000 — 9,300 Miles per second

CORONA BOREALIS — 700,000,000 — 13,400 Miles per second

BOOTES — 1,300,000,000 — 24,400 Miles per second

HYDRA — 2,000,000,000 — 38,000 Miles per second

8. THE RED SHIFT IN THE SPECTRAL LINES. The spectra on the right are those of galaxies pictured on the left. The clear white vertical lines above and below each spectrum are those of a comparison spectrum of a source of light at rest. The horizontal arrows show the amount of displacement of the K and H lines of calcium from their standard positions when the source is at rest. The change in wavelength, or red shift, has been converted into a velocity by the Doppler formula (3).

9. THE 250-FOOT STEERABLE RADIO TELESCOPE AT JODRELL BANK, MANCHESTER. The dipole can be seen at the focus of the paraboloid.

(British Official Photograph: Crown Copyright Reserved)

10. THE CRAB NEBULA. This object is about 4,000 light-years from the Earth. It was formed by a supernova explosion seen on Earth in A.D. 1054.

11. **THE ANDROMEDA GALAXY M31.** This is a typical spiral galaxy. It is comparatively near—two million light-years away. It is 100,000 light-years across, and contains about 100 billion stars. Foreground stars of the Milky Way are evenly distributed over the Plate.

12. A SPIRAL GALAXY, M81.

the evidence

4

astronomical
measurements of distance

DISTANCES AND ANGLES

The central problem in astronomy has always been the measurement of distance. The difficulty is to know whether one is looking at a bright object a long way off, or at a dim one nearby.

The Greeks at about 300 B.C. were able to find the distance of the Moon from the Earth,* and until the seven-

---

* This was a great achievement, considering how elementary their instruments were, and the method was very clever. The essential step was to estimate the diameter of the Moon by using the time it took to cross the shadow of the Earth during an eclipse of the Moon by the Earth. Having found the Moon's diameter, they obtained its distance by the method of apparent size, described later in this chapter.

teenth century this remained the only heavenly body whose distance was accurately known. In 1672 a good determination of the Sun's distance was made, and this was extremely important because, with the aid of a law discovered by the German astronomer J. Kepler in 1618, it enabled the distances from the Sun of all the planets to be found. The distance of a star was first measured by F. W. Bessel in 1838.

Although astronomers have this persistent problem with distances, they are very good at measuring angles. Their bread-and-butter occupation is the measurement of the angular separation of celestial bodies. This means the determination of the angle between the lines of sight of two bodies. The astronomer can find this angle even though he may have no knowledge whatever of the distances of the bodies. Consider, for example, Figure 3. If P and Q are two stars at different distances from the point A, an observer at A can still speak of the angle PAQ as the angular separation of P and Q. Another useful measurement illustrated in Figure 3 is the angular diameter of a body. For a sphere like the Sun, this is the angle subtended at A by the ends of a diameter.

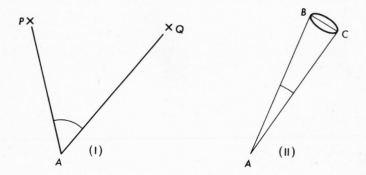

Figure 3. ANGULAR MEASUREMENTS. Figure 3(i) shows the angular separation at the observer A, of the two stars P and Q, namely the angle PAQ. In Figure 3(ii) the angle BAC is the angular diameter, as seen at A, of an object with circular cross-section.

The Sun's angular diameter at the Earth is about half a degree.

By measuring the angular separations of bodies in the sky, astronomers of antiquity found that some, notably the planets, changed their positions relative to the others. The latter became known as the fixed stars. We now know that there are no such things as fixed stars, but we still use the term to denote very distant stars, whose angular separations relative to one another do not change, or change only very slowly. Relative to this background the members of the solar system, and also the nearby stars, show changes in position which enable us to find their distances.

MEASUREMENT OF SHORT DISTANCES

Astronomers measure short distances by the same method that surveyors use, known as triangulation. Thus the distance of the Moon is found as follows: Two observers widely separated on the Earth's surface measure the angular position of the Moon in the sky relative to the fixed stars. For simplicity we suppose that the observers A and B, the Moon, M, and the center of the Earth, C, all lie in the same plane. (See Figure 4.) The observers then determine the angles MAZ_1 and MBZ_2. (Z_1 and Z_2 are points in the sky, called zenith points, directly

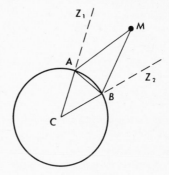

Figure 4. MEASUREMENT OF THE MOON'S DISTANCE. The observers A and B on the Earth's surface measure the angles MAZ_1, and MBZ_2. Knowing the radius of the Earth, and their difference in latitude, angle ACB, they can calculate the distance of the Moon.

over the observers' heads, which they determine by suspend-
ing plumb lines.) The difference in latitudes of the observatories gives the angle *ACB,* and knowing the radius of the
Earth, we have all the necessary information to calculate by
trigonometry the distances *MA, MB,* and *MC* (the last being
strictly the one sought).

The essence of the method is to use the known base line
AB, in conjunction with certain angular measurements, to
find an unknown distance, *MC.* For the method to give
accurate results, the base line must not be too small compared
with the distance to be measured. It can be used to give the
distance of the Sun or the nearer planets, but not the stars.

To find the distance of a star we have to use as base line
the distance between extreme positions *A* and *B* in the Earth's
orbit around the Sun, *S* (Figure 5). At the star *P,* the diameter of the orbit subtends the angle *APB.* Suppose for simplicity that *P* is symmetrically placed in relation to *A* and
B, so that *AP = BP:* then the angle *APS* (which is half the
angle *APB*) is called the *parallax* of the star. Knowing the
angle *APS* and the distance *AB* (which is 186 million miles),
we can calculate *PS,* the distance between the star and the
Sun.

In practice the observer measures the position of *P* in the
sky on two occasions at an interval of six months, this being
the time the Earth takes to get from *A* to *B.* The change in

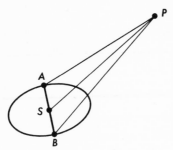

Figure 5. THE PARALLAX OF A
STAR. A and B are extreme positions
of the Earth in its orbit. The astronomer determines the angle APS, which
is called the parallax of star P.

position relative to the background of fixed stars is measured, and this gives the angle *APB*.

Unless the star is fairly near the Earth, say, within 500 light-years, the parallax is too small to be measured accurately. An extension of the method is to use as base line the change in position of the Sun, instead of that of the Earth. We ignore the movement due to the rotation of the Milky Way, and concentrate on the much smaller peculiar motions that stars have relative to one another. The Sun has a peculiar velocity of 12 miles per second relative to the average motion of the stars in our neighborhood. Because the relative distance so moved by the Sun in one year is four times the radius of the Earth's orbit, if we use this annual change in the Sun's position we get a base line double that provided by the Earth's orbital motion (double *AB* in Figure 5).

There are many difficulties in this method. One is that the Sun moves with the speed of 12 miles per second relative to the *average* motion of the nearby stars. This does not guarantee that the Sun will have this speed relative to the particular star we happen to be observing. To overcome this difficulty it is necessary to consider stars in groups and use statistical methods. For this reason the method is called statistical parallax; it can give reasonable estimates of distances up to 1,600 light-years.

THE BRIGHTNESS OF STARS

As we pass to distances such as the diameter of the Milky Way—100,000 light-years—the method of parallax becomes quite hopeless. As Sir James Jeans remarked, the parallax from the Earth's orbital motion for a star at such distances is about equal to the angle subtended by a pinhead at a point across the Atlantic.

To determine the distance of a very remote star, astrono-

Figure 6. THE APPARENT BRIGHTNESS OF A STAR. Light from a star, S, falls on a square of side 1 centimeter, placed at right angles to the beam. The amount of energy falling on the area in one second is called the apparent brightness.

mers use, in one form or another, the *absolute brightness* of the star. This is the power of the star as an emitter of light, or, to be precise, the total amount of energy given out as light in one second. However, what astronomers *measure* is not this, but the *apparent brightness*. This is the power of the starlight *when it enters the telescope;* or, the energy falling in one second on a unit area, perpendicular to the beam of starlight, as illustrated in Figure 6.

It is clear that the apparent brightness depends not only on the absolute brightness but also on the distance; the farther away the star, the less energy will reach the telescope, and the less will be the apparent brightness. The actual relationship is

absolute brightness $= 4\pi \times$ (distance)^2

$\times$ apparent brightness.*   (1)

To illustrate the meaning of these quantities, let us consider the energy output of the Sun. We can measure the amount of energy falling on one square centimeter in a given time by arranging for all that energy to be used in heating

* This formula can be derived as follows: Imagine a large spherical surface, center at the star which is supposed to be radiating at a constant rate; then in one second,

total energy emitted = surface area of the sphere
$\times$ energy falling on 1 square centimeter.

Since the area of a spherical surface is $4\pi \times$ (radius)^2 , it follows that

absolute brightness $= 4\pi \times$ (distance)$^2 \times$ apparent brightness.

some water whose temperature we record before and after. The temperature change gives the total energy absorbed, and from this we can find the amount of energy falling on one square centimeter in one second. This must be corrected for energy absorbed by the Earth's atmosphere before reaching the surface. The result will be the apparent brightness of the Sun. We know the distance of the Sun, so we can calculate its absolute brightness by the use of Formula (1).

In a similar way we can obtain the absolute brightness of any other star if we know its distance. Of course, we would not attempt to find the apparent brightnesses of other stars by using their light to heat water; more sensitive means, such as photoelectric cells, are needed to record the total radiation received.

We can turn Formula (1) round and write it in a different way:

$$\text{distance} = \sqrt{\frac{\text{absolute brightness}}{4\pi \times \text{apparent brightness}}}. \qquad (2)$$

From this we see that if the absolute and apparent brightnesses of a star are known, its distance can be calculated. This is the most useful form of the equation if we are trying to find the distance of a star which is too remote to show measurable parallax.

Unfortunately, our observations of such a star give us only its apparent brightness; the absolute brightness has to be inferred in an indirect way. To illustrate the type of indirect method which is available, let us suppose for a moment that the absolute brightnesses of all stars were the same. Since we know the absolute brightness of the Sun, we should know it for all stars. We could then determine the distance of any star from its apparent brightness, simply by applying Formula (2). Actually, stars vary tremendously in their absolute brightnesses, some being ten billion times more powerful than

others, so this supposition would be quite wrong. Nevertheless, as we shall see in the next section, it was an adaptation
of this idea that produced the first breakthrough in the determination of very large distances.

DISTANCE BY VARIABLE STARS

Certain stars show regular changes in brightness, and these
are called variable stars. It was the properties of these that
made possible the breakthrough in distance determination.
Often the variations are caused by the star pulsating like a
huge lung. The important feature for us is that these stars
act as milestones, enabling us to measure large distances, as
will now be explained.

Most useful are the Cepheid variable stars. Each has a
definite period, which means that if we draw a graph of the
light fluctuations against the time, the curve repeats itself
regularly over and over again. An example of this type of
curve is shown in Figure 7. For some variables the period can
be as short as three hours, but for most it is about seven days.

In 1912 Miss H. S. Leavitt of Harvard Observatory was
studying Cepheids in the Lesser Magellanic Cloud (see Plate
2), which is one of the Milky Way's neighboring galaxies.
She noticed that the period of fluctuation was longer for the
brighter stars. In fact, the graph of apparent brightness
against period is a smooth curve like that shown in Figure 8.
Cepheids in the Lesser Magellanic Cloud can be taken as
equidistant from the Earth because their mutual separations
are negligible compared with the distance of the Cloud itself.
So the effect of distance on the brightness of them all must
be the same, and their absolute brightnesses must lie on a
similar smooth curve.

Before the absolute brightnesses of the Cepheids could be
determined it was necessary to calibrate the curve—that is, to

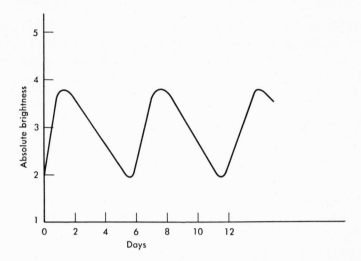

Figure 7. THE FLUCTUATIONS OF A CEPHEID VARIABLE STAR. The rise to the maximum is much steeper than the subsequent fading. The star is about twice as bright at the maximum as at the minimum.

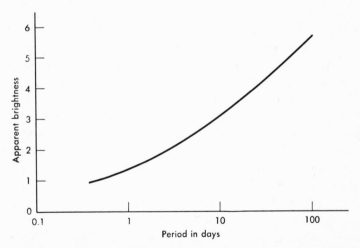

Figure 8. APPARENT BRIGHTNESS OF CEPHEIDS PLOTTED AGAINST THEIR PERIODS OF OSCILLATION. Miss Leavitt discovered that when the apparent brightnesses of the Cepheids in the Lesser Magellanic Cloud are plotted against their periods, the points lie on a smooth curve like the one shown.

31

fix its scale by determining the absolute brightness of at least one of them. The credit for doing this goes to the famous American astronomer Harlow Shapley. It was shown in the previous section that to find the absolute brightness of a star one needs to know its apparent brightness and its distance. Miss Leavitt had measured the apparent brightnesses of Cepheids in the Lesser Magellanic Cloud, but their distances remained unknown because the Cloud is much too remote for parallax observations to be fruitful.

However, there are Cepheids in the Milky Way, and Shapley was able to obtain statistical parallax measurements for some of them. From the knowledge of both the apparent brightness *and* the distance, he was able to determine the absolute brightnesses of these galactic Cepheids by Formula (1). He found too that the galactic Cepheids showed a relationship between period and brightness similar to that found by Miss Leavitt for the Cepheids in the Lesser Magellanic Cloud. It was therefore reasonable to assume that this is a universal characteristic of Cepheids and that all Cepheids of the same period have the same absolute brightness.

The result of Shapley's work was a curve showing the absolute brightness of Cepheids plotted against their periods. This curve has been of tremendous importance in astronomy for the following reason: Suppose one observes a Cepheid with a period of, say, five days; then one can read off from Shapley's curve its absolute brightness, and knowing from observation its apparent brightness, one can calculate its distance from Formula (2). Here is a way of finding the distances of any galaxies in which Cepheids can be detected.

In practice it needed long and patient study before the curve was calibrated; and even then, in the 1920's, many incorrect observations were made because of a complication not properly understood at the time. This is the absorption of light by gas and dust in space, which reduces the apparent brightnesses, and makes the stars seem more distant than they really are. The size of the Milky Way was at first greatly over-estimated because the effect of absorption was neglected.

Nowadays great care is taken to allow for absorption in our own galaxy. The amount of the correction depends on the direction in which one is looking. The strongest absorption occurs in the plane of the Milky Way's disc, where there is an absorbing layer similar to that in the galaxy shown in Plate 7. An anomaly in the color of the light received from a star indicates absorption, and the color of a star is a sensitive check on the presence of absorbing matter in its line of sight.

I shall now summarize the results of this section and the preceding one. To calculate the distance of a remote star, astronomers need to know its apparent and absolute bright-nesses. The former can be measured directly, but the latter is not usually known. However, the absolute brightnesses of certain variable stars, recognizable by their periods, have been determined. Suppose one of these stars is recognized in another galaxy: then by measuring its apparent brightness, and by using the known value of its absolute brightness, we can calculate its distance, and therefore the distance of the galaxy in which it is seen.

A FAMOUS MISTAKE

The Cepheid story was a slow and patient plod toward reliability. Just when the method seemed to have achieved a certain assurance, Baade announced in 1952 that it was giving wrong results by a factor of at least two. Just how dramatic Baade's announcement was for cosmology I shall explain in Chapter 12.

I do not wish to spoil the story by telling it too soon, but this is the place to describe briefly what had happened. In fact, the calibration had been mistaken: the statistical parallax measurements, notoriously difficult to perform, had led to a serious underestimate of the distance of the galactic Cepheids which had been used to calibrate the scale. Indeed these had been estimated to be only half as far away as they actually are, with the result that the distances of all the galaxies had been ascribed half their correct values.

Incidentally, the mistake applied only to Cepheids with longer periods. Those with short periods, plentiful in the Milky Way, were not affected. It was these Shapley had used to chart the Milky Way, so his figures were not affected. Our own galaxy stayed the same, but the rest of the universe became twice as big.

STILL GREATER DISTANCES

Cepheid variables can be identified only in nearby galaxies, and for further ones another criterion is necessary. Hubble found that the brightest star in most galaxies has about the same absolute brightness. The distance of the brightest star in, say, the Lesser Magellanic Cloud is known because we already know the distance of the Cloud, so by Formula (1) of this chapter we can find the absolute brightness of this brightest star. We can use this value of absolute brightness for the brightest stars in *other* galaxies, and obtain their distances, using this time Formula (2). (Actually, the brightest star is sometimes exceptional, and the average of the four or five brightest stars is now more usually taken.)

This method works for those galaxies in which individual stars can be detected, and extends our observations out to a distance of about ten million light-years. Beyond this, galaxies can be seen, even through the most powerful telescopes, only as faint blurs of light on the photographic plate. To estimate their distances, astronomers assume that, on the average, all galaxies have the same absolute brightness. This average can be obtained by taking the mean of the absolute brightnesses of nearby galaxies. Once a figure for the average is available, we can obtain the distance of a galaxy from its apparent brightness, using Formula (2).

In fact, the great majority of galaxies are very faint, so this method of distance measurement is most common. Now, one may object that it is surely very dangerous to assume that all galaxies have the same absolute brightness. Indeed, this would be true if galaxies were like stars, which show enormous variations. However, galaxies are different: most of the nearby ones have absolute brightnesses quite near to the average—nearly all lie between half and twice the average. So it is not such ,a bad approximation to take them as of equal brightness. A factor which helps to correct any mistake in doing this is the enormous number of distant galaxies: it is reasonable to believe that if we take the average our results will be reliable.

DISTANCE IS NOT ABSOLUTE

I have been writing about distance as if it were an absolute quantity with a definite meaning. Small distances, such as those on Earth, do have these properties, at any rate for all practical purposes. To measure the distance between two points A and B on the Earth we could (at least in principle) lay end to end a number of identical measuring rods, and then count them. Numerous corrections, for example, for expansion of the rods due to temperature, would be necessary, but this is merely a technical matter. Moreover, if we measured the distance AB in another way, say, by the surveyor's method of triangulation, we should expect to get the same result.

For cosmological distances these simple ideas do not hold. The distance between two galaxies A and B depends both on how the observer is moving and also on the method he uses to make his measurement. This is basically a result of the theory of relativity, which has dethroned distance from the absolute position it held in classical physics, and shown that both space and time, considered separately, are relative concepts. Because of this, our Formulae (1) and (2) do not strictly apply for very great distances, and have to be replaced by relativistic formulae.

The distance that appears in the formulae is called the "luminosity-distance," because it is based on the brightness of galaxies. I shall illustrate how distance depends on the method of measurement by describing a different way of measuring it. We all know that in our terrestrial experience the farther away an object is, the smaller it appears to be. If we know how big the object really is, we can use this to measure its distance. Suppose it has a spherical shape; then, if we determine its angular diameter, we can find its distance by trigonometry. Although galaxies are not spherical, we can adapt this method to find what is called their "distance by apparent size." Over short distances this is the same as the luminosity-distance, but general relativity tells us that the two are not the same for very great distances.

Indeed, as will be explained in Chapter 7, according to one model of the universe (the Einstein–de Sitter model) the apparent size of a galaxy has a *minimum* value at a certain distance, and galaxies farther away appear larger. If we used the distance by apparent size, there would therefore appear to be a certain maximum distance (namely, that at which the galaxies appear to have the least size), and galaxies with luminosity-distances greater than this would be nearer when judged by their apparent size!

The relativity of distance, though strange to common sense, is not a serious problem to cosmologists. Consider what an astronomer does when he says he is determining the luminosity-distance of a far-off galaxy. He photographs the galaxy and then measures the apparent brightness on the plate. This he converts into a distance by Formula (2), or its relativistic equivalent. Now it is this last step that causes the trouble, and it turns out that there is no need to make it. All the formulae concerning galaxies in cosmology can be written in terms of their apparent and absolute brightnesses, and distance need not enter at all. If the astronomer works in terms of the brightnesses alone, he need make no assumption about what distance "really" is, and can avoid the perplexing problems referred to in the previous paragraphs.

Professional astronomers do in fact use the brightnesses instead of distances when they record and analyze cosmological results. Similarly, a theoretical cosmologist, when relating these results to a particular theory, does not use the idea of distance. Nevertheless, we still find it useful to think in terms of distance sometimes, and provided we remember the limitations, there is no harm in it. It would certainly be hard on nonprofessionals to expect them to give up the concept of distance, and I shall not ask my reader to do it. I ask him, however, to bear in mind that distance is not the absolute quantity which he may have been brought up to believe in. Luminosity-distance is probably closest to our commonsense conception, and it is this I shall use in the remainder of the book.

the principal observations

THE DARKNESS OF THE UNIVERSE

We happen to live near a star, but from the cosmological point of view this is pure accident. To obtain a less special view of the universe, we must look at it at night. Even then we are untypical because we live in a galaxy, and the sky is brighter than for an average observer, who would find himself in extragalactic space. (There is about 10,000 times as much space outside galaxies as there is inside them.)

Let us content ourselves with our galactic night sky. If we look in any one direction, the stars throw no more light than a candle 100 yards away. We are so used to it that we do not find the darkness of the night sky remarkable. But it might have been quite different: the night sky might have been as bright as day.

The first man to recognize that this darkness is significant was the astronomer H. W. M. Olbers in 1826. Olbers investigated a theory of the universe based on what were then very reasonable—indeed, unquestioned—assumptions:

a) the stars are evenly distributed throughout infinite space, and their absolute brightnesses are the same everywhere and at all times;

b) the stars are at rest, except for local random motions;

c) the universe does not change with time.

He then found a very strange result. With these assumptions it turns out that the sky should be everywhere as bright as it would be at the surface of a star.* Thus the sky should be as bright by night as by day, and much brighter than our present day sky.

Olbers was naturally very puzzled by this absurd result derived from such plausible assumptions. At his time it did not seem possible for any of these to be wrong. He concluded that there must be a lot of dust between the stars and the Earth, which absorbs the greater part of the light. We know today that this explanation is not correct: the dust would continually absorb the energy of the light, which would heat it. Eventually the dust would become incandescent, and

---

* Let O be the observer. Consider the stars in a thin spherical shell, center O, thickness t, with inner radius r: then

number of stars in the shell is proportional to r^2,
so amount of light emitted by shell is proportional to r^2,
but amount of light reaching O from one star

in the shell is proportional to $\dfrac{1}{r^2}$.

From this it follows that r cancels out, and the amount of light reaching O from the shell is proportional simply to its thickness t. The same result will apply to any shell centered on O, whatever its radius. Since there are an infinite number of such shells, the total light to reach O is infinite.

This calculation ignores the fact that some light is intercepted on the way by stars between the emitting star and the observer. If account is taken of this, the result is as stated.

would emit as much light as it received. Hence it would have no shielding effect.

In the next chapter we shall see how modern theory has resolved Olbers's paradox.

THE DISTRIBUTION OF THE GALAXIES IN SPACE

Less than four hundred years ago men believed that the Earth was the center of the universe and that the Sun and stars revolved round it. With the growth of detached and dispassionate scientific inquiry, we have come to realize that the Earth and its inhabitants have no special claim to importance; we have learned that our Earth is a smallish planet of an average star in an average position among 10^{11} others in the Galaxy.

With the increased modesty that science has forced upon us, we should not expect our Galaxy to occupy an exceptional position among the other galaxies. We should also be surprised if the part of the universe near us were different, on the average, from the rest. Nevertheless, it would be unscientific to prejudge the issue, and many astronomers have spent years of their lives making and analyzing observations of the distribution of the galaxies. The procedure is to photograph various parts of the sky, using powerful telescopes, and to compare them. If there is no obscuring matter, the number of galaxies would be expected to be the same in equally big regions of the sky. Further, the numbers of galaxies as functions of their apparent brightness should be the same: this means, for example, that the number of very faint (that is, very distant) galaxies should be the same in equal regions.

The observations do show that, on the average, the distribution of galaxies is the same in all directions of the sky—or *isotropic,* as we shall call it. The early observations led astronomers to think that this was not so, because there seemed to be fewer galaxies in the direction of the disc of the Milky Way. We now know that this discrepancy is due to obscuring matter in the Milky Way. If it were not for this purely local circumstance, our telescopes as they sweep across the sky would see the same picture in all directions.

Thus the galaxies are uniformly distributed *in direction*. We now turn to the distribution *in depth,* by which I mean the following: Suppose we count the number of galaxies in a cube with sides of unit length, in various parts of the sky. (Of course, the cube must be a large one: the unit length of its side should be at least ten million light-years.) The distribution in depth is the dependence of this number on how far away from us the cube is. Does this number increase, decrease, or stay the same as the distance increases?

Since we assume that the Milky Way is not in a special position, the expected answer is that the number of galaxies per unit volume (that is, the *density* of the galaxies) should be independent of distance. However, this obvious answer is too simple. There are a number of reasons why we should not be surprised to find the density depending, or seeming to depend, on the distance.

To understand this we must remember that our only measure of the distance of a galaxy comes from its brightness (or that of its component stars). Hence any factor that gives us a mistaken idea of its brightness causes us to mistake its distance. Possible factors of this type are the following:

a) The presence of absorbing matter in space: if we underestimate this we shall tend to think the galaxies are fainter (and therefore more distant) than they really are.

b) The red shift of the light from the distant galaxies, which will be described in detail later in this chapter. This weakens the light and, unless allowed for, will make us overestimate the distances of the galaxies.

c) The fact that we see all galaxies *as they were when the light left them*. In the case of very distant parts of space, this light has been traveling for thousands of millions of years. Now thousands of millions of years ago the absolute brightnesses of galaxies may have been different. Hence, attributing the same absolute brightnesses to all galaxies (even very distant ones) may lead us into error.

Such phenomena do in fact make it appear that the density of galaxies does not remain the same as one sees farther into the depths of space. It is natural to ask whether the density "really" is the same, if corrections are made for (*a*), (*b*), and (*c*). According to the cosmological principle, described in the next chapter, we believe that it does, but we cannot prove this directly because to do so we should need to get an instantaneous view of the universe as it now is. Since light (and other electromagnetic radiation) is the only means we have of observing the universe, we know from (*c*) that this is impossible. I shall return to this point in Chapter 13 when considering the latest results of the radio astronomers, who "see" very far indeed into space and for whom the problem of homogeneity becomes acute.

However, we do know that over distances for which the time of light-travel can be neglected (out to about 100 million light-years) the galaxies are homogeneously distributed.

THE COSMIC DENSITY

By counting the number of galaxies in a known volume, multiplying by the average mass of a galaxy (10^{44} grams), and dividing by the known volume, we can find the average density of matter in space—at any rate for our immediate neighborhood. This turns out to be extremely low, as expected when we take account of the vast empty spaces of the universe: it is about 1 gram in 10^{30} cubic centimeters, that is,

in a cube with edges 60,000 miles long. Another way of looking at it is that the average density of matter in the universe
is equivalent to one atom of hydrogen in a volume of 60 cubic
feet. With the very best vacuum techniques it is not possible
to obtain such rarefied matter in a terrestrial laboratory!

Instead of expressing the density as one gram in 10^{30} cubic
centimeters, we usually write it 10^{-30} grams per cubic centimeter. What this means is 1 divided by 10^{30}, which is a dec-
imal point followed by twenty-nine zeros and then a one.
Here are some more examples of numbers with negative in-
dices:

$$10^{-1} = 0.1, \quad 10^{-5} = 0.00001, \quad 2 \times 10^{-8} = 0.00000002.$$

It is important to notice that 10^{-1} is *greater* than 10^{-2}, which
is greater than 10^{-3}, and so on.

It must be stressed that the figure just given for the density is only a lower limit: it is the density of *luminous* matter,
and any nonluminous matter present is bound to increase it.
Nonluminous matter can sometimes be detected by its ob-
scuration of distant galaxies, but so far no very reliable quan-
titative estimates have been produced. In any case there may
be nonluminous matter which has negligible obscuring effect
—namely, dilute hydrogen gas—and this would be very hard
to observe directly, though it may ultimately be possible to
detect it by means of ultraviolet light which it emits, when
observations can be made from outside the Earth's atmosphere using space satellites or rockets. It is therefore difficult
to estimate the amount of nonluminous matter present in the
universe.

Cosmologists are not agreed on how this uncertainty in
the cosmic density is to be regarded. Some, such as Bondi,
Gold, and Hoyle, the originators of the steady-state theory,
have no hesitation in assuming that the density might be
10^{-29}, or ten times the observed figure. On the other hand,

G. C. McVittie, of the University of Illinois, considers it quite improper to assume the existence of so much unobserved matter, and thinks that theories requiring it should be abandoned.

I shall refer to the cosmic density again in Chapter 14.

THE RED SHIFT

Before describing this famous phenomenon, I must outline some fundamental properties of waves and light.

If one end of a long rope is fixed and the other end is agitated in a regular way, a wave will travel along it. The crests of the wave can be seen moving with a definite speed along the rope, but each particle of the rope moves up and down, and for this reason the wave is called *transverse*. The distance between consecutive crests is called the *wavelength*, and the height of the crests above the average position is the *amplitude* of the wave. (See Figure 9.) The *frequency* is the number of waves passing a fixed point in one second.

For our purposes the reciprocal of the frequency, called the *period*, will be more useful. This is defined as follows. Consider an observer O who watches the waves at a certain point. Let O note the times at which two successive crests pass him; then the difference between these times is the

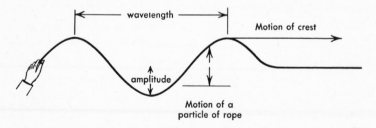

Figure 9. PROPAGATION OF WAVES ON A LONG ROPE. The wave travels along the rope, but each particle of the rope moves transversely up and down.

period of the wave. In the case of the rope, the period is equal to the time the experimenter takes to move his arm once up and down.

The period, the wavelength, and the speed of the forward motion of the wave are related by the formula

$$\text{velocity} = \frac{\text{wavelength}}{\text{period}}.$$

Light consists of transverse waves resulting from oscillations in the strength of electric and magnetic fields in space. In the nineteenth century physicists were very worried because there was no medium for the oscillations to occur in—nothing corresponding to the rope. They invented a substance called the ether—an all-pervasive but intangible fluid—which was supposed to vibrate when light traveled. The properties of this hypothetical substance were worked out in great detail.

Many attempts were made to detect the ether. The most famous was in 1887 when A. A. Michelson and E. W. Morley carried out an experiment to find the velocity of the Earth relative to the ether. The Earth moves about the Sun with a speed of $18\frac{1}{2}$ miles per second, so presumably it has a speed relative to the ether. The Michelson-Morley experiment, however, gave a zero speed, not once but many times. This led to the fantastic conclusion that the Earth is always at rest in the ether, while the rest of the universe has motion relative to it. But this was tantamount to putting the clock back three hundred years and supposing that the Earth is the center of the universe. The alternative was to give up the ether, and this course was eventually adopted.

As there is no ether, we have to accept that light waves travel through completely empty space. The vibrations which constitute light are different from vibrations of the rope, or the vibrations which make sound, because both these involve something material that vibrates. The idea that energy can be transmitted by light waves, even though there is nothing material to carry it, was strange at first, but is now universally accepted. Here is just another example of common sense confounded by the march of physics.

The color of light depends on its wavelength, ranging from red with the longest wavelength through the colors of the rainbow to violet with the shortest. All light waves are short—there are 14,000 in one centimeter for red light, and 25,000 for violet. The wavelengths of light occur so often in calculations that physicists use a special unit of length for them, called the Ångstrom, abbreviated to Å., which has the value

$$1 \text{ Ångstrom} = 10^{-8} \text{ centimeter } (= .00000001 \text{ cm.}).$$

In terms of Ångstrom units the wavelength of violet light is about 4,000 Å., and that of red light about 7,000 Å. White light, such as we receive from the Sun, is not a pure color, but a mixture of wavelengths.

Of all electromagnetic waves, those to which the eye is

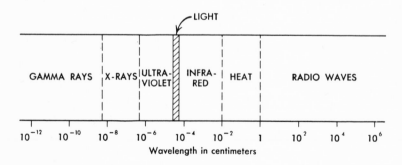

Figure 10. SPECTRUM OF ELECTROMAGNETIC WAVES. The figure shows the approximate ranges of wavelengths for radiation of various types. For example, waves of heat have lengths between about 0.01 cm. and 1cm.

sensitive (and which we call light) form only a very small part. In fact, any wavelength is possible, depending on the nature of the disturbance causing it. Infrared radiation and heat are formed of longer waves, and radio waves are longer still—one centimeter or more long. In Figure 10 is shown a diagram of the spectrum of electromagnetic waves. All these waves travel through empty space with the speed of light— 186,000 miles per second.

Light, and all electromagnetic waves, have one very remarkable property. Consider a man on a train firing bullets. To a man on the ground, the speed of the bullets depends not only on the power of the gun but on the speed of the train as well. With the light waves composing the flash it is different: these travel at 186,000 miles per second *relative either to the gunman or the observer, whatever the speed of the train!*

This fact, apparently so contradictory to common sense, is the cornerstone of the special theory of relativity. This theory is so well verified by experiment (it is confirmed daily in cyclotrons) that the hypothesis of the constancy of the velocity of light, although it has not been verified *directly,* must be regarded as proved because its consequences are so well established.

Although the speed of light does not depend on the speed of the source, the *wavelength* does. This is called the *Doppler effect* (after Christian Doppler, the Viennese physicist who discovered it), and is illustrated in Figure 11. A source, moving with velocity V, emits light which is observed by O, who measures the period of its vibrations. At the beginning of a period the source is at S_1, whereas at the beginning of the next period it has moved on to S_2, more distant from O. Because of the greater distance, the wave now takes longer to reach O, and the period that O measures is longer than if S

were at rest.* The period being longer, the wavelength as measured by O is also longer. In fact, the law of the Doppler effect is

$$\frac{\text{increase in wavelength}}{\text{normal wavelength}} = \frac{\text{speed of source}}{\text{speed of light}} \,. \qquad (3)$$

The ratio on the left-hand side is the famous *red shift,* so called because the increase in wavelength means that the light is reddened. Notice that the red shift is the fractional increase, or, if we multiply by 100, the percentage increase. The Doppler law states that it is proportional to the speed of the source: if this speed is doubled, the red shift is doubled, and so on.

The preceding paragraph refers to a source receding from the observer. If the source is approaching, a similar argument shows that the period, and the wavelength, are reduced. This means that the color of the light is shifted toward the violet.

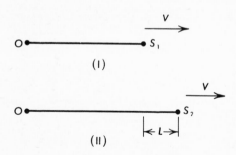

Figure 11. THE DOPPLER EFFECT. (i) and (ii) show the position of the moving source S at the beginnings of two consecutive periods. During the emission of one complete wave the source recedes a distance, L, from the observer, O.

---

* Let T be the time of one normal period of vibration. Then since in time T, S travels a distance L, we have $L = VT$. Hence the light emitted at the end of the vibration has to travel an extra distance VT, and since it is moving with the speed of light, c, it takes a time $\dfrac{VT}{c}$ to do so. Hence the increase in period due to the recession is $\dfrac{VT}{c}$, and

$$\frac{\text{increase in period}}{\text{normal period}} = \frac{VT}{c} \div T = \frac{V}{c} \,.$$

Since wavelength $= c \times$ period, this leads to the formula for the Doppler effect (3).

In cosmology the red shift is overwhelmingly more important than the violet shift.

The Doppler effect is a thoroughly well-established piece of physics. It has been verified not only for light waves but also for sound waves. Indeed, anybody can verify it qualitatively for himself by noticing how the pitch of a jet aircraft changes as it approaches and recedes.

I mention that the Doppler effect is respectable physics because some people think that when used in cosmology it is highly disreputable and suspect. So it is as well to be clear that the effect itself is above suspicion: the argument concerns the way cosmologists use it, and I shall discuss this at length later on.

In the case of light it is not easy to observe the Doppler effect on earth because the ratio

$$\frac{\text{speed of source}}{\text{speed of light}}$$

is usually quite negligible on account of the enormous speed of light. The heavenly bodies have speeds very much higher than those of terrestrial objects, and in astronomy the Doppler effect is used a great deal. A star in the Milky Way may be moving with a velocity of, say, 20 miles per second away from the Earth so that the above ratio is 20/186,000, or 0.0001. Hence, even in this case the increase in wavelength is only one part in ten thousand of the normal wavelength. Nevertheless, the increase can be detected. It will be well to describe briefly how such tiny shifts in wavelength are measured. To do this I shall give a brief account of spectrum analysis.

SPECTRUM ANALYSIS

It was Isaac Newton who first showed that white light can be decomposed into the colors of the rainbow. He did this by allowing the light to pass through a glass prism. This is the principle of the *spectroscope,* which analyzes light into its constituent colors; and the picture so formed is called the *spectrum* of the light. As we move along the spectrum in the direction of increasing wavelength, we pass from violet through the colors of the rainbow to red at the other end of the visible spectrum.

The spectrum of sunlight is a continuous band of colors, containing a number of dark lines. Each line is formed because certain atoms in the outer layers of the Sun have absorbed light of a particular wavelength so that this light is missing, leaving the gap. There is a vast number of these absorption lines, but some are especially sharp and black, and these characterize the Sun's spectrum. They can be compared with spectra of laboratory sources of light, such as an iron arc. In this way many of the lines can be assigned wavelengths with great accuracy, and then the wavelengths of the remainder can be deduced.

So accurate can this comparison of lines be made that it is possible to tell when a star's spectrum is showing a very small Doppler effect. The spectrum allows us to calculate the left-hand side of Equation (3), and so obtain the speed of the star. The first to use this method was the British astronomer Sir William Huggins, who was able to announce in 1868 that the star Sirius was receding from the Earth at 29 miles per second.

HUBBLE'S LAW

The method can also be applied to the galaxies, and it is here that the most exciting results have emerged. The first galactic spectrum to be analyzed was that of the Andromeda galaxy, which in 1912 was found by V. M. Slipher to be approaching us with a speed of 125 miles per second. Slipher proceeded to study the spectra of other galaxies, and found that most of them were shifted toward the red end, indicating a recession from the observer. These were the first measurements of the red shift of the galaxies (Plate 8).

The work was taken up by M. Humason at the Mount Wilson observatory, using the 100-inch reflecting telescope, then the largest in the world. Over a period of years, he observed many fainter (and therefore more distant) galaxies; all showed a red shift, and moreover *the red shift increased with the distance.* Using the Equation (3) for his red shifts, Humason calculated the speed of recession of the more distant sources as no less than 25,000 miles per second, or one-seventh of the velocity of light.

During the 1920's Humason was working with Edwin Hubble, the most famous of all cosmologists. Together in 1928 they discovered the law connecting the red shift of a galaxy with its distance, now called Hubble's law. This states that the red shift is directly proportional to the distance from us:

$$\text{red shift} = \text{constant} \times \text{distance}. \qquad (4)$$

"Constant" here means a fixed number, the same for all galaxies; its value is now believed to be about 10^{-10}, distances being measured in light-years. The law implies that if one galaxy is twice as far away as a second, its red shift is twice as great. The distance, of course, has to be found by the indirect methods of measurement described in Chapter 4, in which the apparent brightness is used.

The establishment of Hubble's law required great ingenuity and patience. This was particularly so because the instrumentation was primitive compared with that in use today. G. J. Whitrow has described how Humason, working with the 100-inch telescope, managed to obtain red shifts from galaxies so faint that they needed to be photographed con-

tinuously for ten nights. To do this the telescope had to be
fixed on a tiny point source for all this time—which, of
course, meant that because of the rotation of the Earth, the
telescope had to be rotating at precisely the same rate in the
opposite direction. The result of this was a picture perhaps
one-tenth of an inch long and one-thirtieth of an inch wide,
and on this the spectral lines had to be identified, and the red
shift measured!

Although Hubble's law is accurately fulfilled for the
nearer galaxies (out to hundreds of millions of light-years),
astronomers are not agreed that it is strictly true at the greatest distances now accessible to observation. W. A. Baum of
Palomar Mountain, who has recently observed one extremely
distant galaxy with a red shift of 0.46 (which means, according to the Doppler formula, that it has a speed nearly half
that of light), considers that Hubble's law may well be true
even at the enormous distance of three or four billion light-
years. However, according to A. R. Sandage, the red shifts
do not accurately follow the law at these very great distances.
The correction, if any is needed, will take the form of an
additional term on the right-hand side of Equation (4) in-
volving the square or higher power of the distance. We shall
return to this question in Chapter 13.

I mentioned that the first galactic spectrum measured
showed a violet shift, and so indicated that the galaxy was
approaching us. Looking back, we can say that this was rather
ironic, since the vast majority show a red shift and are receding. However, the early cosmologists of Slipher's time and
shortly afterward noted that several galaxies showed violet
shifts, and they wondered whether the universe really was
expanding.

The explanation of these violet shifts has since become
clear. It is now known that, whereas clusters of galaxies recede from other clusters, the galaxies in each particular clus-

ter form a comparatively stable configuration, except for what are called their peculiar motions. These peculiar motions are governed by local gravitational fields, and have nothing to do with the expansion of the universe. For members of our own cluster, the Local Group, the peculiar velocities are as likely to be velocities of approach as of recession, and so there is nothing surprising in the fact that some of the spectra show violet shifts. For more distant galaxies, in other clusters, the peculiar velocities are not large enough to cancel out the velocity of cosmic expansion (which, by Hubble's law, is larger the greater the distance), so the overriding motion is one of recession.

IS THE RED SHIFT A DOPPLER EFFECT?

I have tacitly been supposing that a red shift implies a velocity of recession. However, Hubble's law is, precisely speaking, expressed in Equation (4), which is a statement of what is observed,* and which says nothing at all about velocity. It will therefore be well to analyze carefully our assumptions before we take the comparatively well-established law of Hubble and infer definitely from this that the galaxies are receding.

Our reason for doing so is that Equations (3) and (4) together lead to

$$\frac{\text{speed of source}}{\text{speed of light}} = \text{constant} \times \text{distance of source}, \qquad (5)$$

so that the source (that is, the distant galaxy) has a velocity away from the Earth. In other words, if we interpret the red shift as it would be interpreted in the laboratory, or in observations of nearby stars—that is to say, as a Doppler

---

* Even more precisely, apparent brightness rather than distance is what is observed (as explained at the end of Chapter 4), and this should appear on the right-hand side of Equation (4). However, for clarity I continue to refer to distance as a direct observable.

effect—we are led to the conclusion that the galaxies are rushing away from us. This is the celebrated *expansion of the universe*. I shall be writing at length about this in the next chapter; for the present I want to consider our justification in interpreting the red shift as a Doppler effect, because there have been many competent people, though not many working astronomers, who have believed and still do believe that the red shift does not imply the expansion of the universe.

One reason for believing that the red shift is a Doppler effect is the negative one that nobody has ever proposed a convincing alternative explanation. It has been suggested that the reddening might be due to scattering of light by intergalactic dust, which would have a reddening effect just as dust has in the terrestrial atmosphere at sunset. However, this explanation will not work because the scattering would blur the images of the distant galaxies to such an extent that we should not see them as points of light as in fact we do. Other suggestions, for example that light changes its wavelength in some mysterious way on its long journey through intergalactic space, do not count as explanations since they have no theoretical basis, and lead to no new predictions which could be used to verify them.

The fact is that the Doppler effect is the only possible scientific explanation of the red shift at present. But cosmologists do not believe in the expansion of the universe just on these negative grounds. There are excellent positive reasons as well.

The Doppler law states that a given recession velocity causes a *fixed* percentage change of wavelength, the same for all wavelengths. This is clear if we multiply both sides of Equation (3) by 100, so that the left-hand side gives the percentage increase in wavelength. It means that if the velocity is one-tenth the speed of light, then a wavelength of 1,000 Å.

is increased by 10 percent, that is by 100 Å., one of 2,000 Å. is increased by 200 Å., one of 5,000 Å. by 500 Å., and so on. Thus the shift is not a bodily one—the whole spectrum is not shifted to the red by the same amount of, say, 100 Å. Nor does the shift affect only certain wavelengths—it affects the whole spectrum of electromagnetic waves.

These properties of the Doppler effect are characteristic, and any other cause of reddening is likely to affect different wavelengths in another way. Now, *the red shift of the galaxies follows precisely the percentage Doppler law*. This has been checked over a wide range of colors (that is, wavelengths) in the visual spectrum. This is indeed strong evidence that the red shift is a Doppler effect, that is, that the universe is expanding.

It is noteworthy too that so long as the red shifts are small, nobody doubts that the Doppler explanation is correct. The use of this on the spectra of stars is a routine business, and astronomers constantly in this way infer velocities of stars moving toward or away from us. But, when the velocities become large, some scientists seem to lose the courage of their convictions and refuse to follow the clear path offered by the evidence.

Let us freely admit that the expansion of the universe on the scale now revealed by modern red-shift measurements is an awesome conception. We have to imagine vast conglomerations of billions of stars hurtling through space at speeds of up to 80,000 miles per second. Further, as we shall see later, we have to face the possibility that the universe is in transition from a state of unimaginable temperature and density to an emptiness in which the Milky Way, and a few galaxies of the Local Group, will be the only galaxies left in the visible universe. There is no doubt that the expanding universe, in its vastness and in its consequences, challenges the human imagination.

Much of the opposition to the explanation of the red shift as a Doppler effect is, I believe, due to the difficulty of accepting the enormous velocities of the distant galaxies. However, as G. J. Whitrow has pointed out, these velocities become less remarkable when considered in relation to the size of the objects moving. Let us consider the time taken by each of the following moving bodies to pass through a distance equal to its own diameter:

Earth (in its orbital motion about the Sun), 7 minutes;

Sun (in its orbital motion about the Galactic center), 100 minutes;

a receding galaxy moving at 20,000 miles per second, 1 million years.

This shows that galaxies recede comparatively slowly, when account is taken of their sizes. Of course, this argument proves nothing—but since I believe that the opposition to the expanding universe is psychological, I feel entitled to counter it with a purely psychological argument!

Finally, I should mention that the radio counts, described later in this chapter and in Chapter 13, cannot be convincingly explained on the basis of a universe without expansion. These observations are entirely distinct from the red-shift measurements, and give quite independent confirmation of the expansion of the universe.

From now on I shall assume that the red shift of the distant galaxies is a Doppler effect. This implies that the universe is expanding, and it forms the basis for the work in the next chapter.

PRACTICAL DIFFICULTIES OF THE RED–SHIFT OBSERVATIONS

The object of this book is to give an educated person a broad account of cosmology without worrying him with technical details. I am therefore loath to enter into the practical difficulties which confront astronomers engaged in their daily work. Nevertheless, I should be deceiving the reader if I were to suggest that the verification of Hubble's law, even today, is anything but an extremely complicated business. I therefore give a brief account of these difficulties: then if in the future some unlikely catastrophe happens and Hubble's law needs serious revision, I can at least say that I warned my readers. For we cosmologists are now very cautious people as a result of the notorious revision of the distance scale in 1952, which plays in the history of our subject much the same part as the crash of 1929 in the history of Wall Street. The reader can, if he wishes, skip the rest of this section, since it will not be needed in what follows afterward.

The problems arise mainly in determining the distances of the galaxies whose red shifts are being measured, for the red shifts themselves can now be determined with great accuracy. Indeed, for very distant galaxies the red shift is (because of Hubble's law) very large, and more easily measurable. As astronomers jokingly say, it could be measured with a foot rule. But for distance measurements the reverse is true: the more distant the galaxy, the fainter it is and the more unreliable the measurement of the apparent brightness. Indeed, matters are much worse than this, because the red shift itself weakens the light, as well as changing its wavelength.* Moreover, since the sensitivity of photographic plates depends on the wavelength of the incident light, the reddening affects the image on the plate. This latter difficulty requires a correction, known as the K-term, to be made to the measured

---

* In fact, the red shift has a doubly weakening effect. In the first place, since the period of the incoming waves is increased, their frequency is reduced: this diminishes their energy according to Planck's formula:

$$\text{energy} = \text{Planck's constant} \times \text{frequency}.$$

Second, the lowering of the frequency means that not so many arrive in one second, so that the energy received is still further reduced.

brightness to obtain the brightness which would be recorded if the photographic plate were equally sensitive to all wavelengths.

As if all this were not bad enough, the corrections themselves are not at all straightforward. They depend on the cosmological theory one adopts, which itself, of course, depends on the corrected measurements!

Obviously, these corrections to data, which to start with consist of very faint specks of light, make the investigation of Hubble's law extremely difficult for the very distant galaxies. For such reasons there are still many unsettled questions in observational cosmology.

RADIO TELESCOPES

As was stated earlier, the eye is sensitive to only a tiny part of the electromagnetic spectrum. With instruments we can detect invisible radiations of various sorts, for example, X rays, ultraviolet light, and infrared rays. However, much of this radiation is absorbed by the Earth's atmosphere, so we receive little of it from stars. (To astronomers one of the most exciting possibilities of the space-research programs is that of getting observations of stars and galaxies without interference by the atmosphere. It is unfortunate for cosmology that the telescopes required to observe the most distant galaxies are so enormous that it will be some time before we can hope to get one of them into outer space.)

There is, however, one band of radiation other than light which can penetrate our atmosphere. This is a wide band of radio waves, of length from about 1 centimeter to 100 meters. There is a good deal of emission by stars (and other heavenly bodies too) on these wavelengths and in recent years the science of radio astronomy has made great progress in the study of such waves.

In visual astronomy we supplement our eyes by telescopes, which are instruments for collecting light waves emitted by celestial bodies. We have no organs for perceiving radio waves, so radio astronomy has to be done entirely by instruments, known as radio telescopes. The usual principle of the radio telescope is the same as that of the reflecting optical telescope. In both cases a curved mirror is used to concentrate the incoming rays by reflecting them to a focus. For most purposes the best mirror to use is a paraboloid,* because in this case the focus is a single point. Figure 12 illustrates the focusing of rays from a distant source by means of a parabolic mirror.

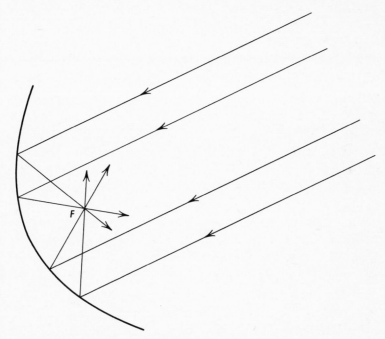

Figure 12. FOCUSING BY A PARABOLIC MIRROR. Parallel rays from a distant source are concentrated on to the focus, F.

* A paraboloid is the surface obtained by rotating a parabolic curve (shown in Figure 23 [i]) about its axis.

For the reflection of radio waves, sheet metal or metal mesh is used. At the focus is placed an electronic device called a dipole, the function of which is to absorb the concentrated waves. These are then amplified and recorded continuously as a graph showing the strength of the waves plotted against time. The type of record obtained is shown in Figure 13. The small ripples come from irregularities in the performance of the electronic components of the instrument and from small fluctuations in the cosmic radio background, and are referred to as noise. The large peak is due to a celestial source of radio waves, coming into the beam of the telescope either as the Earth rotates or as the telescope is swept across the sky. A radio telescope is tuned to receive radiation of a certain definite wavelength; for example, the waves recorded in Figure 13 were about two meters long.

Perhaps the most famous radio telescope is the parabolic

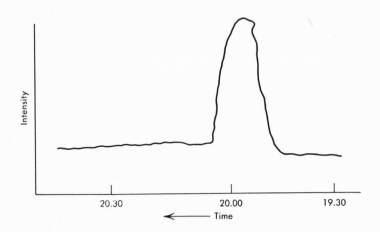

Figure 13. THE RECORDING OF A RADIO TELESCOPE. The large peak indicates a celestial source of radio waves which transits the instrument at about 20.00 hours. The ripples are due to noise in the instrument and to small changes in the cosmic radio background.

reflector at Jodrell Bank, Manchester, England, which is 250 feet in diameter, and is at present the biggest of its kind in the world. (See Plate 9.) The "dish" of the instrument is steerable and can be pointed in any direction of the sky. The total weight of the superstructure is nearly 2,000 tons, and 10,000 tons of reinforced concrete were used in the foundations to make the instrument stable. The cost of such a telescope is greatly increased by the fact that, for the focusing of the beam to be accurate, the whole area of the 250-foot dish must be truly parabolic to within half an inch. Moreover, when the telescope is pointing in different directions the stresses due to gravity are differently distributed, so there is a distortion which depends on the inclination to the horizontal. This too must be kept within the half-inch tolerance.

The steerable dish is not the only type of radio telescope. There are now several fixed reflectors set in holes in the ground; these have no stability or distortion problems, and they are much cheaper than steerable dishes of the same size. Of course, they suffer from a lack of maneuverability. There is a considerable advantage in working two or more radio telescopes of the same kind in conjunction, and they then make up what is called an interferometer. The great drawback of radio telescopes is the inaccurate readings they give for positions of objects in the sky, and interferometers minimize this defect. Most radio work of cosmological interest has been done with interferometers.

THE RADIO PICTURE OF THE UNIVERSE

The picture of the universe as "seen" by a radio telescope is strangely different from the optical one. To start with, it can be seen equally well whether the sky is clear or overcast because radio waves easily penetrate cloud. It can also be seen equally well at night or day: this is because, whereas optically the radiation from the Sun is so powerful that it makes all the stars invisible, the radio-Sun is much weaker. The latter has a hazy outline owing to the strong radiations from the corona. As explained in Chapter 2, the planets and the Moon are easily visible because of the Sun's reflected light; but its radio emission is so weak that the other bodies of the solar system are hardly detectable by radio, except for Jupiter. Jupiter has a radio source of its own, the cause of which is at present unknown; it is extremely powerful, and operates mainly on wavelengths between 10 and 20 meters. However, it is not likely that the Jovians have a broadcasting station. Jupiter, like the Earth, has an atmosphere, and it is thought that this may contain electrically charged particles producing synchrotron radiation (see below).

Very few of the famous stars known to man since the dawn of history can be seen by their radio emission, but there are many different radio stars, some extremely powerful. Also the Milky Way has a halo, invisible optically, so that its radio-shape is more like a sphere, as shown in Figure 14.

CAUSES OF THE RADIO EMISSION

Why does the Milky Way have a halo according to its radio emission, but not according to its visual picture? The

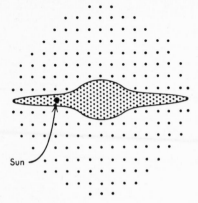

Figure 14. THE MILKY WAY AS "SEEN" BY RADIO. Radio emissions are obtained from the central disc, and the radio picture of this resembles the optical one (See Figure 2). There is, however, a spherical region enclosing the disc, from which only radio emission comes, called the halo around the Galaxy.

Sun

answer lies in the different origins of radio and light waves. Almost all light comes from hot bodies, which give out radiation because of changes taking place within their atoms. Radiation emitted from hot bodies in this way is called thermal. Now, some radio waves are thermal—for example, some of those from the Sun are emitted just because the Sun is hot. However, thermal radiation is much more powerful at short wavelengths, so hot bodies tend to emit light and other shortwave radiation, rather than radio waves—that is, visually bright stars are much weaker as radio emitters.

The most interesting radio sources are not thermal ones at all; they produce radio waves by a quite different mechanism. Consider first the waves transmitted by a broadcasting station: these result from oscillating electric currents which are made to flow in the transmitting aerial. Now, an electric current is really a flow of electrons, that is, of charged particles. In other words, the radio waves are produced by the motion of charged particles in the aerial.

The fact that accelerated charged particles emit electromagnetic waves has been known for a long time: this is a classical phenomenon predating the quantum theory, and predicted by the equations formulated by Clerk Maxwell a century ago. It happens frequently in "atom-smashing" machines called synchrotrons, which accelerate charged atomic particles by means of magnetic fields. For this reason, radiation of this type is often nowadays called synchrotron radiation.

Radio astronomers believe that a great deal of the cosmic radio emission is synchrotron radiation. The theory is that charged particles, mainly electrons, are accelerated by magnetic fields which are thought to be present in space between stars. The gas in which these particles are moving is quite cold and dilute, and the difference between this emission and the thermal emission from a hot, dense star could hardly be greater.

The Galactic halo is one of the places where synchrotron radiation is produced, and this is why it is detectable on radio, but not on visual wavelengths. Many other well-identified sources are also believed to be the result of synchrotron radiation.

One of the strongest radio sources is what is called the Crab nebula, which can be seen in the telescope as a patch of light containing a number of filaments (see Plate 10). By good luck the origin of this nebula is known to have been a violent stellar explosion seen on Earth in A.D. 1054. We know this because it was carefully recorded by Chinese astronomers of the day. It must have been a most dramatic event, because in spite of its distance of 4,000 light-years, the exploding star was for several months brighter than Venus, the nearest planet, and was visible during full daylight.

An exploding star such as this is called a supernova. When, owing to some instability in its interior, a star becomes a supernova its brightness may increase 100,000,000 times, and gas is hurled off in all directions. Supernovae are rare, and only three are known to have taken place in the Milky Way: the one of 1054, one in 1572 observed by the Danish astronomer Tycho Brahe, and a third seen by Kepler in 1604. They can be seen happening in other galaxies, but owing to the distance their appearance is not spectacular.

The force of the 1054 explosion was such that today, more than 900 years afterward, the remnants are still flying apart with a speed of about 800 miles per second. These remnants form the Crab nebula. This is still bright visually for its size, but it is as a radio source that its power is remarkable. The puzzle was that so much radiation came from what seems to be largely gas: but if the gas consists of charged particles, then the violent motion will lead to synchrotron radiation, and this will be sufficient to make the nebula a very powerful radio source. It is now generally accepted that this is the mechanism for the Crab nebula, and other very powerful radio sources.

THE TRIBULATIONS OF A RADIO ASTRONOMER

For cosmologists the Crab nebula is on our doorstep, so to speak, and it is natural to ask what radio astronomy has to say about more distant objects. We find that it has much to say of the greatest importance but that we have to take what we hear with a grain of salt. We are getting wary of radio astronomers who jump the gun and speak before they should.

Whatever criticisms we make of radio astronomers, we must have sympathy with them in their problems. First, their science is a very new one; it began in 1932 when Karl Jansky of the Bell Telephone Laboratories published his findings on the receipt of radio noise from outer space, but it did not really get going until after the Second World War. Second, there are tremendous difficulties, compared with optical astronomy, arising from the difference in length of radio and light waves. These I shall try briefly to explain.

With a telescope one can see as separate objects a collection of things which to the naked eye appears only as a blur. This property of the telescope is known as its *resolving power:* this is a measure of the angular separation of two objects which can just be distinguished. Resolving power is proportional to

$$\frac{\text{wavelength of light}}{\text{diameter of aperture of telescope}},$$

the aperture being simply the opening through which the light comes. The smaller this ratio, the better the resolving power. Now, since the wavelength of light is very short—about 5×10^{-5} centimeter—it follows from the formula that good resolving power can be obtained with moderate aperture sizes, say, up to 200 inches, the diameter of the Palomar telescope.

The same formula applies to radio telescopes, but for them the wavelength is about one million times as great. Therefore to obtain comparable resolving power, radio astronomers would have to increase the diameters of their instruments one millionfold! They do their best by using enormous reflectors like the 250-foot dish at Jodrell Bank, but to obtain the same resolving power as that of the 200-inch optical telescope, the reflector would have to be more than 3,000 miles in diameter! By using interferometers consisting of separate radio telescopes several miles apart, radio astronomers make big improvements in resolving power over that of the single dish, but even so the results necessarily fall far short of the precision achieved by optical astronomers.

What this means in practice is that radio astronomers find it hard to resolve a signal into its constituent sources. Thus there is a tendency for them to think that sources are more powerful than they really are—because what they take for a single source may be several sources near together in the sky.

Other more technical difficulties arise, connected with the intricate electronics of the instruments. (A radio astronomer probably needs to know more about electronics than about astronomy.) One particularly malevolent property of early radio telescopes was that their aerials were sensitive in directions where they should have been insensitive. This sometimes led to completely bogus radio stars.

Surveys of radio stars have been published by various observatories, and there has been little agreement among the results. In particular the surveys of the observatory at Sydney, Australia, have disagreed with those at Cambridge, England. It is now thought by F. Graham Smith of Cambridge that of 2,000 radio stars listed in the Cambridge survey of 1953–1954, no fewer than 1,500 were wrong in position or intensity or both. Later observations of radio astronomers still show an alarming measure of disagreement.

HOW FAR DO RADIO ASTRONOMERS ''SEE''?

In spite of these uncertainties, it now seems clear that several hundred radio point sources have been located in the sky with fair precision. The obvious next thing to do is to search for these with optical telescopes to find out what they look like.

In some cases this identification between radio and optical images has been made. One example is the Crab nebula, and another is a very powerful source, called the Cygnus A source, which was located first by its radio emission, back in 1944. At that time positioning in radio astronomy was very crude indeed, and the Cygnus A source could not be pinpointed sufficiently to identify it with any star or galaxy that could be seen in the telescope. It was not until 1951 that a position could be given by the radio astronomers sufficiently accurate for their optical colleagues to look seriously for the visual identification in the 200-inch telescope.

When Baade at Palomar Mountain searched for the source, he found a very remarkable thing. At just the right place there appeared on the plate *two* galaxies so close together that they must be colliding. It seems therefore that *this radio source is caused by the collision of two galaxies.*

A collision of galaxies sounds like a hair-raising event, but astronomers believe it to be a little less cataclysmic than it sounds. They believe that the stars pass through unchanged, except for a few near misses which get deflected from their course. The real collision takes place between the clouds of gas and dust in the two galaxies. In the course of the million years for which the collision lasts, the gas and dust become violently agitated, and radio waves are generated, probably by the synchrotron process described earlier. This description is confirmed by the Palomar Mountain observations, which show that the gas is very hot, at a temperature of about 10,000 degrees centigrade, and in turbulent motion.

The important point here is the enormous power of the Cygnus A source. Since its distance is known from the optical measurements of its red shift, it is possible to estimate its total power. It turns out that the radio waves alone contain as much energy as the *total* radiation of all forms emitted by a normal galaxy. When we remember that long waves, such as radio waves, are much less energetic than short waves,* like light or X rays, we understand that this is a very powerful emission.

Some other galaxies which emit radio waves have been identified optically. These include several colliding galaxies, and a few nearby galaxies, such as the one in Andromeda, M31. However, *most of the powerful radio sources cannot be identified optically with anything at all.* When the optical telescopes are pointed in the direction of these radio sources, nothing of note is seen. This is the strangest feature of the whole of radio astronomy.

Why are these sources invisible? This question is perhaps the most controversial in astronomy today. Some astronomers think that the sources are mainly just stars or gas clouds in the Milky Way which for some unknown reason do not emit light; or perhaps they are nearby invisible galaxies. But another group has a much more exciting answer: *the sources are invisible because they are so distant.* In other words, radio telescopes are seeing much farther into space than optical ones.

---

* This follows from Planck's law:

$$\text{energy} = \text{Planck's constant} \times \text{frequency};$$

since the frequency of radio waves is low, so is their energy.

Let me assemble the arguments which support the second answer. First, there is one quite direct piece of evidence. One radio source, 3C 295, discovered by radio astronomers at Cambridge, England, which *has* been identified optically, turns out to be about 4,000 million light-years away. This is the galaxy with a red shift of 0.46, studied by Baum and referred to earlier in this chapter. There is nothing conspicuous about 3C 295 optically, and it would not have been noticed if the radio astronomers had not called attention to it. The enormous distance of this galaxy—it is the most distant one known—shows that radio telescopes are certainly seeing a very long way.

In this controversy we are once again up against the old problem of determining distance. For 3C 295, radio astronomers were lucky enough to get a reliable estimate from their optical colleagues, who determined it by measuring the red shift and then applying Hubble's law. When there is no optical identification, radio astronomers have to proceed, much as optical astronomers do, to estimate the distance of a source by the energy received from it. They have to use Formula (2) of Chapter 4, suitably amended:

$$\text{distance} = \sqrt{\frac{\text{radio power emitted}}{4\pi \times \text{radio power received}}}.$$

The power received is known, but how do we estimate the power emitted?

Martin Ryle, at Cambridge, whose work we shall consider shortly, assumes that the unknown sources have about the same power as the Cygnus A source, the distance of which is known. Hence the distances of the unknown sources can be calculated. They are found to be extremely large, many of them much larger than any distance that has ever been measured by optical telescopes. This is the chain of reasoning which leads many astronomers to suppose that these radio sources are extremely distant.

The crucial step in the argument is the assumption that the unknown sources are about as powerful as Cygnus A, and it is this that Ryle's opponents dispute. They point out that if Cygnus A is exceptionally powerful, the other sources may be weaker, and therefore nearer than Ryle calculates. Against this, and on Ryle's side, we know that 3C 295 is even stronger than Cygnus A, which suggests that Cygnus A may not be exceptional. Further, one may ask: if these radio galaxies are really quite near, why do we not see them? I feel that Ryle's opponents must give us an answer to this question.

I do not wish to bewilder the reader with further details of the dispute. I shall now give a brief account of Ryle's work, to be supplemented in Chapter 13 when we come to consider how it helps to decide between rival theories.

RADIO ASTRONOMY AND COSMOLOGY

Through optical telescopes we see galaxies distributed isotropically—that is, the same in all directions. If the powerful radio sources are really distant galaxies, and not just local stars, their distribution too should be isotropic. This is what Ryle finds, and it does at least show that the sources are outside the Milky Way; because if they were not we should see more of them in one direction than another on account of our off-center position, shown in Figure 14.

Let us assume Ryle's sources are galaxies. How can this help cosmology? Optical astronomy's most important cosmological measurements are those of the red shift, which lead to Hubble's law. Unfortunately, radio astronomers cannot yet measure the red shift of distant galaxies. This is because if they receive waves of length, say, one meter, from a distant galaxy, there is no way of knowing what the wavelength was when the radiation left the galaxy. There is nothing corresponding to the sharp spectral lines of light emitted by well-identified atoms.

There is, however, an investigation radio astronomers can make which is of the greatest interest to cosmologists. This is the relation between the density of galaxies in space and the distance, which was mentioned earlier in this chapter. To put it in another way, consider a large spherical volume of space, center the Milky Way, and radius r light-years. Suppose we count the number of galaxies inside this sphere, and call it N. If we take now a sphere with the same center and different radius we get, of course, a different value of N. By taking a series of different values of r, and finding the corresponding values of N, we can plot a graph of N against r. The result is of fundamental importance to cosmology, and offers a way of deciding between various theories of the universe.

Essentially what Ryle has done is to plot this graph for us. In practice, his procedure is a little different. Instead of plotting the number of galaxies against the distance, he plots it against the power received from them by the radio telecope. The technical name for the latter is the flux density, and it is denoted by S. The details of Ryle's graph, along with the conclusions we can draw from it, will be described in Chapter 13.

THE "AGE OF THE UNIVERSE"

Not so long ago many people believed that the universe was created by God in 4004 B.C. This date had been announced in 1658 by Archbishop Ussher of Armagh, Ireland, who was prepared even to state the precise day, namely, Sunday, October 23rd. The date was pushed back several thousand million years by the geologists of the last century, and astronomers are now pushing it back even further.

The concept of creation arises in cosmology in this way. Certain cosmological theories lead us to think that the expansion of the universe began with a gigantic explosion. If these theories are correct, the Earth and the stars cannot have existed at that time because the temperature of the explosion was so high that they would have been dispersed into their separate atoms (strictly into protons, electrons, and other atomic particles). The time which has elapsed since the explosion—let us call it T years—must evidently be greater than the age of the Earth and stars as found by geology and astrophysics. Thus these latter ages give us a lower limit for T, and this will rule out those cosmological theories which predict too small a value of T.

Some cosmologists call T the "age of the universe." I am prepared to put up with this term as a picturesque synonym for "the time since the expansion started," but I want to emphasize that there is no evidence whatever that the universe has a finite age, and I do not believe for a moment that it had a beginning. As we shall see later, in the relativistic theories there is difficulty in tracing history back for more than T years, but in my opinion this is due to the inadequacy of our theories, and not to the absence of history. The "age of the universe" is liable to become a dangerously misleading concept, and to show my disapproval of it I shall keep it in quotation marks.

The age of the Earth is determined nowadays from radioactive rocks. Radioactive matter decays at a rate which is proportional to the amount of matter left at any given moment; for example, uranium disintegrates ultimately into lead and helium in this way. The rate of radioactive decay is found to be completely independent of changes in temperature and other physical conditions. Therefore, by measuring the amount of radioactive substance remaining, and the amounts of the disintegration products present, geologists can assign an age to the rocks. By this and similar methods the age of the Earth is found to be about 4,000 million years.

Information about the ages of stars is harder to obtain, but recently some estimates of age have been made by astrophysicists working on stellar structure. This latter subject is an extremely difficult one because all that is really observed of stars is their exteriors, and from this the whole structure of the interior has to be inferred. As Fred Hoyle once said, it is like trying to deduce the composition of a chimney sweep from the color of his skin.

An important tool in studying the structure of a star is its color. It is believed that stars tend to change color in a systematic way as they get older. This must be a result of changes in the internal structure which take place as the hydrogen in the star is converted into helium by thermonuclear processes. Hoyle and others have used the theory of these processes to trace the evolution of a star, including its surface temperature on which its color depends. By making certain assumptions about the initial composition of the stellar material, they are able to estimate how long the star has taken to reach its present color.

The first calculations using this method, published in 1955, gave about 6,000 million years as the age of the oldest stars in the Galaxy, and also in some other galaxies. Since then, astrophysicists have tended to push this age upward, and at the present time several workers think that the figure should be 10,000 million years, or even more. It is quite clear, however, that the theory is in an uncertain state. It depends very much on the nature of the nuclear reactions which are assumed to take place in the deep interior of the star, and knowledge of these is naturally somewhat speculative. Moreover, the presuppositions concerning the initial composition of the material out of which the star condenses are hardly more than guesses at present.

I therefore think that it would be a mistake to attach very much importance to the figures at this stage. I shall adopt a conservative estimate of 5,000 million years as the least age of the oldest stars in the Galaxy, and also in some other galaxies, bearing in mind that this may be an underestimate. It follows, therefore, that the "age of the universe" must be greater than 5,000 million years.

SUMMARY OF THE OBSERVATIONS

To help the reader in sorting out the essentials, I summarize the important observations which a cosmological theory must account for.

1. The darkness of the night sky: that we are not drowned by a flood of light from the distant galaxies.
2. The isotropy of distribution of the galaxies, and the fact that, at least locally, the distribution is homogeneous; also that the average density of matter in the universe is not less than about 10^{-30} grams per cubic centimeter, although it may be considerably greater.
3. Hubble's law that the galaxies recede from us with speeds proportional to their distances away.
4. The radio observations relating the number of galaxies within a certain region of space to the radius of the region.
5. The "age of the universe," which is greater than 5,000 million years.

Further information about these observations will be given in Chapter 13, after we have considered how cosmological theories try to explain them.

the theories

6

the expanding universe

THE COSMOLOGICAL PRINCIPLE

In the last chapter, I explained why cosmologists, almost without exception, believe that the red shift of the light from the distant galaxies indicates that they are receding from us. It is time to give a picture of what this means on a cosmic scale.

At first sight this seems to imply that we are at the center of the universe and that for some mysterious reason the Milky Way acts as a center of repulsion. This would be quite contrary to the modesty which three centuries of science have forced upon us—we no longer think that our Earth or, come to that, our Galaxy, has any special place in the universe. So strong is our conviction on this point that cosmologists have embodied it in what is called *the cosmological principle*, which states that *a galactic observer situated anywhere in the universe must at a given time observe essentially the same picture as ourselves*. By a galactic observer is meant one who is moving with the average speed of matter in his neighborhood: he must not be moving too fast relative to his own galaxy, or the effects of the special theory of relativity operate, and the universe would look different.

In interpreting the cosmological principle we must think on a grand scale. For example, that one observer may live on a small galaxy, and another on a large one is, of course, a trifling local matter, to be neglected when they compare their world pictures. What the cosmological principle means is that all galactic observers will discover sets of observations like those described in the summary of Chapter 5, and these will at a given time be the same for all of them.

The cosmological principle is an assumption, and might be wrong. We have no chance of verifying it directly because we cannot go to another galaxy and take a look at the universe from there. The method of verification has to be the indirect one often used in science: we make inferences from the principle and check these by observation. The inferences include all the cosmological theories described in this book— except the steady-state theory which uses a different formulation of the principle: this I shall give in Chapter 12.

HOW THE EXPANSION LOOKS

We see the galaxies receding away from us in all directions, as if we were at the center of the universe. Hence according to the cosmological principle, *every galactic observer sees himself at the center of the universe*. The universe is a place with "its center everywhere and nowhere." This is strange to our common sense because we are used to thinking of bodies, like the Earth or the Sun, which have a unique center. It becomes less strange if we think of the universe as *infinite*. We should then hardly expect it to have a center, because it has no boundary and so we cannot define a center. In an infinite universe we can more easily imagine that all points would be equivalent. However, a finite universe can have the same property, as will be explained in the next section.

There is also the problem of the recession itself: that every galactic observer must see the other galaxies receding directly from him. This is hard to visualize at first. For example, in Figure 15 we have to imagine galaxy G receding directly from all three galaxies A, B, and C; that is, to each of A, B, and C, G must appear to move along a different dotted line.

We can see that this is possible if we remember that A, B, and C are themselves moving. Look at the cube in Figure 16(i) which has A, B, and C at the corner, and G at the center. Imagine it to undergo an overall expansion so that it grows into Figure 16(ii). G has now receded from each of A, B, and C, and these have receded from each other. This is what mathematicians call an isotropic expansion. One can simulate it easily by stretching a solid block of rubber equally in three perpendicular directions. (Though, of course, one cannot do this experiment with an infinite block!)

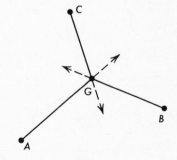

Figure 15. THE RECESSION OF GALAXIES. An observer on any of the galaxies A, B, or C sees the galaxy G receding from himself. (See also Figure 16.)

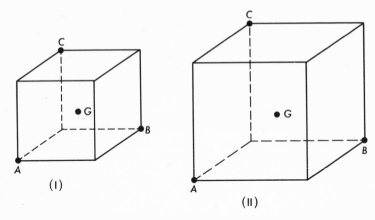

Figure 16. THE EXPANSION OF THE UNIVERSE. If the cube with center G is imagined to expand, G will appear to recede from each of the galaxies A, B, and C.

CURVED SPACE

I realize that this section heading may make the reader close the book—or, worse still, not buy it! For some reason or other, the words "curved space" are anathema to a large number of intelligent people who grasp the most abstruse concepts in science but consider higher mathematics beyond them.

Yet there really is nothing mysterious about curved space. Indeed, what we live on, the surface of the Earth, is a two-dimensional curved space, and it has the following interesting properties:

a) it is finite in area;

b) it has no boundary, and no center;

c) if you go far enough you are liable to come back to where you started.

These properties are so commonplace that we take them for granted, but I shall need them later on.

"But," you may say, "it's a trick. We really live in three-

80

dimensional space, and this is quite different. It is infinite in volume, and if you go straight you will never come back to your starting point. The Earth is just a surface immersed in this three-dimensional space." I agree, but let me ask you to do what mathematicians do, and accept a convention. This convention is that we stick to two-dimensional surfaces for a moment and call these spaces. Then you will admit that a curved space like the surface of the Earth is no harder to think of than a flat space like a table top. (In fact it may even be rather simpler because a spherical surface has no problems with infinity as an unbounded plane has.) And, by the way, there are occasions when we think more naturally in terms of the curved two-dimensional Earth's surface than of the three-dimensional space in which it is immersed: thus when we say it is 3,000 miles from New York to London, we mean over the surface of the Earth, and not along a hole bored through the interior.

We need now to make the jump from two-dimensional to three-dimensional curved space. I do not ask you to *visualize* the latter—I do not believe anybody can do that, not even the most hard-bitten geometer—I ask you simply to admit it as a possibility. If we need a picture, we shall have to think of our familiar two-dimensional case. Of course, analogies like this are a danger, but mathematicians, by the use of abstract symbols and formal proof, can guard against it.

The reason for giving this description of curved space is that the space of the universe *may* be curved, though the observations are not yet accurate enough for us to be sure. What would it mean if the three-dimensional space we live in were curved, and how would we detect it? It would mean that the elementary properties of the Euclidean geometry we learned at school would not be verified experimentally: for example, the sum of the angles of a triangle would not be 180 degrees. This leads us into deep water because a triangle has three *straight lines* for its sides: how does one draw a straight line in a curved space? The answer is that you take the line of shortest distance between the end points, which is called a geodesic. Mariners and airline pilots habitually take geodesics on the Earth's surface,

Although there would be departures from Euclidean geometry if three-dimensional space were curved, we know that this would not be a good way of studying the curvature, because these effects would be much too small. The great German mathematician Karl Friedrich Gauss, who first had the idea that our space might be curved, studied a triangle formed by three mountaintops. He was disappointed to find that the angles added up to 180 degrees. It is only on the cosmic scale that differences from Euclidean geometry begin to show up, if indeed they do at all. This is not surprising: we should expect curved three-dimensional space to be locally almost flat (that is, Euclidean), just as locally the Earth seems to be flat, and its curvature becomes apparent only if one goes on a long journey.

I can now return to a point mentioned in the previous section. A finite universe need have no center in the ordinary sense, provided it is curved. We can see this from the analogy of the two-dimensional Earth's surface which has no center (or every point can be regarded as the center) although it is finite.

One last thing about curved space should be noticed. Some curved spaces, like the surface of a sphere, are finite in extent, but others are infinite. For example, the surface obtained by rotating a parabola (Figure 23[i]) about its axis is infinite in area. We shall meet both sorts of curved three-dimensional space in the next chapter.

THE EXPANDING UNIVERSE AND OLBERS'S PARADOX

Olbers's paradox was that the night sky is dark, whereas, on the assumptions which he made, it should be as bright as at the surface of the Sun. We can now see where Olbers went wrong: he assumed that the stars have no systematic motions, whereas owing to the expansion they are in radial motion away from the observer. This motion has the effect, as explained in Chapter 5, of weakening the light. For the distant galaxies (which contribute most of the light because there are so many of them) the weakening is very considerable because the radial velocities are enormous. The total result is that the amount of light received at an arbitrary point in space is reduced so much that the night sky is dark. Thus one of Olbers's hypotheses was incorrect, and his conclusions invalid. The expansion of the universe satisfactorily disposes of Olbers's paradox.

THE START OF THE EXPANSION

Let us look at the expansion in a very naïve way. Suppose that each galaxy is moving with constant speed relative to us and that it has had this speed ever since the expansion started. We do not believe this is strictly true, but it will simplify matters to assume it for the moment. If from our observations we know the speed of a certain galaxy G, and its distance, then, on the assumption that the speed has not changed, we can say how long ago it was since the distance between us and G was zero. In fact,

$$\text{time} = \frac{\text{distance of } G \text{ from us now}}{\text{speed of } G}. \tag{6}$$

Let us call this time T. Suppose we carry out the calculation for another galaxy; we shall find that its time turns out to be the same as G's. Indeed, from Hubble's law we can prove that *all galaxies had zero distance from us at a time T ago.**

Our simplified interpretation of Hubble's law therefore leads to the conclusion that all galaxies were compressed together in a very small volume of space T years ago. In fact, as we shall see in the next chapter, the theories say that the density of matter was infinite at that time, and the universe was in what mathematicians call a "singular state." Without paying too much attention to this at the moment, we shall find it helpful nevertheless to regard T as the time during which the expansion has been going on. From the observations we find that Formula (6) gives approximately

$$T = 10^{10} \text{ years (10,000 million years):}$$

that is, *the expansion of the universe started 10,000 million years ago.*

This time is consistent with the evidence presented in the last chapter. We saw that our Galaxy is 5,000 million years old or more. If the expansion started from a state of high temperature and pressure, all matter would be split into its constituent nuclear particles, and the galaxies must have formed later. Thus our naïve theory is in comfortable agreement with observations on this point.

Finally, we shall consider what was neglected in our assumption that the other galaxies keep constant speeds relative to our own. This unaccelerated motion could occur only if gravity were inoperative; in fact, gravitation must slow the expansion down, particularly in the early stages when the

* This follows from Equation (5) of Chapter 5, which may be written:

$$\frac{\text{distance of source}}{\text{speed of source}} = \frac{1}{\text{constant} \times \text{speed of light}}$$
$$= \text{same for all galaxies}$$

galaxies are close together. However, it turns out, as will be seen in the next chapter, that this neglect of gravitation does not lead to a great error in the value of T, so our simplified picture is quite useful.

To improve on it, we have to consider the general theory of relativity, which is the modern theory of gravitation. Indeed, general relativity is much more than a theory of gravitation: it is a theory of space, time, and motion as well. All these are vital ingredients of the cosmological problem, and so cosmology is most naturally treated as part of general relativity. This treatment I shall attempt in the next chapter.

simple relativistic models of the universe

THE GREATNESS OF EINSTEIN

In 1900 a young man left the Polytechnic at Zürich at the age of twenty-one. He had graduated, but without particular distinction; he had annoyed several of his professors by neglecting the formal part of his studies, and was refused an assistantship at the Polytechnic after his graduation. Indeed, he had some trouble in getting a job at all, and for a time had to make do with minor schoolteaching posts. However, in 1902 he obtained the position of technical expert, third class, in the Swiss Patent Office.

Such were the modest beginnings of the career of Albert Einstein. Nevertheless, the job in the Patent Office left him time and energy to carry on independent research, and by the time he gave up his job in 1909 he had acquired a world-wide reputation.

Einstein's prolific genius produced great theories in half a dozen different branches of physics. Any one of these would have been enough to stamp him as an outstanding man of his time. Together they rank him as one of the greatest minds of all ages, and make him the peer of Newton, and of Archimedes of antiquity.

His name is always associated with relativity, and by agreement among physicists this is his finest work. It is surprising, therefore, to find that he was awarded the Nobel prize for his contributions to the quantum theory. Though there is no doubt whatever that this work deserved the prize, the committee's reason was grotesque: the prize is awarded for discovery in physics, and there was doubt whether a mere theory such as relativity counted as a discovery!

Relativity is really two theories—special and general. Special relativity arose at the beginning of this century, and Einstein's paper of 1905 is commonly considered to have originated it. The matter is not clear cut because the subject was "in the air," and others, notably Henri Poincaré and the Dutch physicist H. A. Lorentz, also grasped dimly that a revolution was about to take place in physics. But Einstein realized more clearly than the others what he was about, and pressed home the new ideas with great boldness and vigor.

If the discovery of special relativity was a matter for the photo finish, in the case of general relativity it was Einstein first all the way and the others nowhere. He produced the theory in 1915, and for many years few of his fellow physicists could understand it. There were distinguished exceptions such as the British astronomer and mathematician Sir Arthur

Eddington, and the Dutch astronomer W. de Sitter. The world of physics realized that a bomb had exploded but was too dazed by the force of the explosion to pick up the pieces.

Gradually the new ideas spread to a wider circle, and physicists and mathematicians began to work out the consequences of the intensely mathematical general theory. Developments were slow, and it was nearly twenty years after Einstein's discovery before the cosmological consequences of his work were thoroughly appreciated. Even now, after nearly fifty years, there is a wealth of knowledge still to be dug out of Einstein's equations. We think that at last we have a fairly good understanding of what Einstein's theory means for cosmology, though shortcomings in our knowledge will become clear later.

THE THEORY OF RELATIVITY

Relativity has one central idea: the importance of the observer. Before Einstein, no one had thought seriously about the place of the observer in physics. It had always been assumed that although all real observers are fallible, and are liable to get different results, it made sense to speak of the *absolute* result which would be found by some godlike observer, detached from the everyday world.

The great Isaac Newton recognized the problem when he put forward his theories of mechanics and gravitation. These theories were founded on the ideas of Absolute Space and Absolute Time, and Newton knew he could not say what these were or how to find them. What clock measures Absolute Time? There is no answer. The philosophers criticized Newtonian physics, but such was its wonderful success that the scientists paid no heed. And just as well, for it was Newton's theories more than anything else which transformed Europe from the Middle Ages to modern civilization.

But the difficulty remained and nagged away at the more thoughtful physicists long after Newton's death. Put in a more concrete form, the problem is this: An observer measures the positions of objects relative to some standard, which we call his frame of reference; this is just like marking a position on a map. In three dimensions it is often convenient to think of an observer carrying about imaginary scaffolding, the intersections of which serve to mark the positions of objects. Such scaffolding is called a frame of reference or a coordinate system. Now suppose there are two observers, *A* and *B*, each with his own frame of reference but in motion relative to one another, and suppose both are equipped with laboratories and both do experiments. Which one will find the ordinary laws of physics correct? Or perhaps both will? Or perhaps neither?

According to Newton, the observer for whom his laws were designed was one at rest in Absolute Space and using a clock measuring Absolute Time; others were liable to find that the laws did not work. Now it was known that the laws worked to high accuracy for ordinary terrestrial observers, so there was no practical problem; but to those of a philosophical turn of mind the question was: What is the true Newtonian absolute frame of reference?

In the second half of the nineteenth century scientists thought that this absolute frame was provided by the ether, the nonviscous fluid which was supposed to pervade all matter and space. As explained in Chapter 5, the ether was also thought to be the medium in which electromagnetic waves vibrate, and it was relative to the ether that light was supposed to have its velocity of 186,000 miles per second.

The Michelson-Morley experiment, which showed that the ether did not exist, destroyed the nineteenth century absolute frame of reference, and restored the problem to precisely the form in which it had faced Newton.

This was the situation when Einstein entered the field in 1905. His solution was bold and simple. To the question "How can we find the absolute frame of reference?" Einstein answered, in effect, "We can't, because it doesn't exist." This was not a new trick in mathematics and physics: when men have tried and failed to solve a problem for hundreds of years it has often been fruitful to ask in the end "What follows if our problem has *no* solution?" Einstein's genius was to be able to carry through the investigation and to produce workable theories based merely on an impossibility—that of finding an absolute frame of reference.

The theory of relativity acknowledges that frames of reference are relative, and that one is as good as another. Its program has been to cast the laws of physics in such a way that they hold equally for all observers, whatever frame of reference they use. What is almost incredible is the riches that have turned up alongside the road to this seemingly austere goal.

Einstein first implemented his program in a special case—hence the special theory of relativity. Suppose two observers *A* and *B* are on their own in empty space, far from forces like gravity, and that neither has any rocket engines. We then speak of them as *inertial observers,* because they are moving simply under their own inertia,* and their frames of reference are called *inertial frames.* Inertial observers are either at rest relative to each other, or they move relative to each other with constant speed in straight lines. According to relativity it must be possible to formulate the laws of physics so that they apply equally to both *A* and *B*. The formulation of the laws in this way constitutes special relativity. In Chapter

---

* The inertia of a piece of matter is the property whereby it tends to resist a force accelerating (or decelerating) it. If no forces act on it, there is nothing to resist, and it goes on moving with constant velocity.

5 I mentioned one of the consequences of special relativity—that the speed of light has to be the same for all inertial observers.

Special relativity deals only with inertial frames of reference. General relativity is the extension of relativity to *all* frames. Einstein found that to carry out this program he had to bring in gravitation. From the assumption of the relativity of all reference frames there sprang a new theory of gravitation which improved even on the near perfection of Newton's theory, and, for the satisfaction of the philosophically minded, was free from the logical flaw of Absolute Space and Time.

It was shown by H. Minkowski, who had been one of Einstein's teachers, that special relativity is much simplified if the three dimensions of space and one of time are treated together, instead of separately as in classical physics. The result is called the space-time continuum, and it has four dimensions. In general relativity the four-dimensional method is imperative, and space and time are intricately woven together by Einstein's equations. Cosmologists are fortunate because, in their particular use of the equations, space and time can be separated, and an unambiguous meaning given to them.

The gravitational field is one of the three fundamental fields of force, the others being the electromagnetic and the nuclear fields. General relativity is called a *field theory,* because it describes the gravitational field, and Einstein's equations of general relativity are called field equations. Progress in relativity is made largely by finding solutions of them. A number of solutions are known, though far fewer than relativists would like. Luckily, these include several that apply to the cosmological problem, and it is on them that the relativistic theory of the universe is based.

MODELS OF THE UNIVERSE

Each cosmological solution of the field equations gives us a model of the universe, by which is meant an account of the history of the universe. Of the many models available, only one can be correct, as we have only one actual universe. Owing to the uncertainty of the observations, it is not yet possible to decide which model is the correct one, so I shall describe several models because any of them might turn out to be correct. Moreover, it is interesting to study the behavior of different models in order to see all the possible sorts of universe we might have had.

When I speak of the history of the universe I am really being rather grandiloquent. Since the universe means literally everything we can know, its history would, strictly, include everything in the ordinary history books of this and every other planet! Of course, I do not mean a detailed history of this sort, but an account of the past and future of the very large-scale features of the universe—say, of the clusters of galaxies.

The use of models is very common in physics, and may be likened to the use of maps in geography. The model, like the map, is acknowledged to be an oversimplification, but is intended to describe certain features of whatever it is supposed to represent. An astrophysicist's model of a star, in which different layers of matter are arranged in neat concentric spheres, is not a precise representation of any real star, but it helps him to understand certain features of stellar structure that he regards as important. In the same way, a road map will not usually indicate the width of the roads, or all their curves and gradients, but it enables a motorist to find his way. The type of model that a physicist will use for any given object depends, like the cartographer's map, on the purpose he has in view: for example, in geophysics the Earth may be represented as a large inhomogeneous sphere, whereas in astronomy it is usually represented simply as a point with mass and position.

A cosmological model is intended to represent the positions and motions of the clusters of galaxies. It does this by prescribing a certain expansion curve, to be described shortly. For relativistic cosmological models, this curve is obtained from solutions of Einstein's equations. In somewhat the same way, astronomers calculate the positions and motions of bodies of the solar system from Newton's dynamic equations,* and this constitutes their model of the solar system. In this case it is even possible to make mechanical models, such as the projectors in planetaria. We cannot make a mechanical model of the universe (because to do so would require either infinite space or curved space, or both), but the model given by our expansion curve is an adequate substitute.

The basic feature in the history of the universe is the expansion, since this is the reason for the large-scale changes. We can trace the expansion in the following way. Let us fix attention on two typical galaxies A and B, and suppose that at a certain moment the distance between A and B is 1 unit: the unit could be any large distance, say 100 million light-years. Before this moment the distance AB will be less, and afterward it will be greater. Let us use the abbreviation R to denote AB; then R depends on the time, and we can express this dependence in a graph. If we had chosen two other galaxies, C and D, a different distance apart, and taken CD as the unit distance, then the same graph would give the variation of CD with time.

Different models give different graphs for the dependence of R on the time, and I shall use these graphs to distinguish between them.

* Small corrections are required for the effects of relativity.

THE EINSTEIN–DE SITTER MODEL

In Figure 17 the graph of the scale function R against time represents the Einstein–de Sitter model of the universe, the simplest relativistic model.* It will be seen that R increases rapidly from zero, and although it always increases, the rate of increase becomes less rapid as time goes on. For example, if our typical galaxies A and B were at unit distance 5,000 million years after the start of the expansion, then after 7,500 million years the distance AB is 1.31, and after 10,000

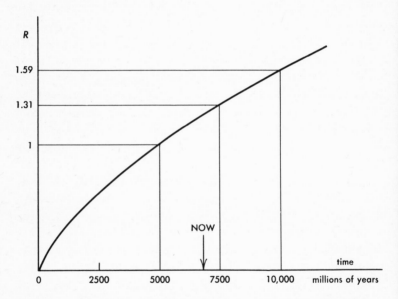

Figure 17. THE EINSTEIN–DE SITTER MODEL. The scale function R is taken to have the value unity 5,000 million years after the start of the expansion. "Now" indicates the time which, according to the model, has elapsed since the singular state.

* It should not be confused with the Einstein model or the de Sitter model, both of which will be referred to later; the model described in this section was a joint creation of Einstein and de Sitter.

million years it is 1.59. Thus at this stage the expansion is not very rapid, as it takes 2,500 million years for distances to increase by less than one-third.

The Einstein–de Sitter model starts from a "singular state." This means that the scale function R is zero, so that the distance AB was zero, and the distances between all pairs of galaxies were zero. Matter was so closely packed that the density was infinite. Now the volume of space in the Einstein–de Sitter model is infinite, so we have to imagine an infinite universe packed solid with matter of infinite density suddenly starting to expand in such a way that later the density becomes quite small. This strange picture arises if we take the singular state too literally, and certainly does not correspond with reality. In Chapter 8 I shall try to explain what the singular state really represents.

According to the model, the present time is about 7,000 million years after the singular state. This is rather less than the "age of the universe" as given by our simple theory described at the end of Chapter 6, because the Einstein–de Sitter model takes account of the slowing down of the expansion by the mutual gravitation of the galaxies.

As stated, the Einstein–de Sitter model is the simplest one that conforms with general relativity. The geometry of space is Euclidean (that is, flat) which means that space has the ordinary properties of school geometry—for example, the angles of a triangle add up to 180 degrees.

Nevertheless, the model has some strange features. For example, suppose we measure the apparent sizes of galaxies and plot them against their distances. As a measure of apparent size astronomers take the angular diameter, defined at the beginning of Chapter 4. We should expect, of course, that the farther away a galaxy is, the smaller it would appear to be. This is not so for large distances in the Einstein–de Sitter model. Near to the observer, the galaxy does appear smaller the farther away it is, as in ordinary experience. But as more distant galaxies are examined, there comes a point at which the apparent size reaches a minimum value. The apparent size of galaxies farther than this point *increases* with the distance. Hence there should be a certain minimum angular diameter of galaxies, according to this model. Here is a way of checking the Einstein–de Sitter model which may soon yield some results.

Another interesting property of the Einstein–de Sitter model is how far one can see in it. Of course, the observer is supposed to be provided with an ideal telescope, and we neglect any absorption of light by dust and gas. It turns out that even such a well-equipped observer could see only a limited distance. The horizon beyond which the observer could not see would recede with time, so more and more of the universe would become visible as time passed.

The cause of the horizon can easily be understood. As only a finite time has elapsed since the singular state at the start of the expansion, light can have traveled only a finite distance since then. This distance is the maximum over which an observer can see. As time passes, light travels farther, and so the maximum increases.

The density of matter in the model falls steadily with time. This means that the number of galaxies per unit volume decreases, so that the distances between them increase, and the model becomes more sparsely populated. The total number visible in an ideal telescope increases, however, owing to the receding horizon.

THE CYCLOIDAL UNIVERSE

I want now to describe a very different model, though still a comparatively simple one, which I shall call the *cycloidal universe*. The curve of the scale function R graphed

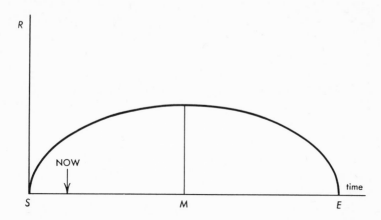

Figure 18. THE CYCLOIDAL MODEL. The present epoch, calculated from the theory of the model, is indicated by "Now." After the moment indicated by M the model begins to contract.

against time is shown in Figure 18, and is called a cycloid. The first thing we notice about it is that instead of increasing indefinitely as in the Einstein–de Sitter model, R increases to a maximum and then decreases to zero again. Let us trace the history in terms of the separation of our two typical galaxies A and B. This starts from zero at S, just as it did in the Einstein–de Sitter model; but after increasing rapidly at first, it continues to increase but much less rapidly, until after time M the increase stops altogether, and AB has a maximum value. Thereafter AB begins to decrease, and the rate of decrease grows continually, until at E, the distance between A and B is again zero.

It is the event E which is the most remarkable feature of the model. Both S and E represent singular states, S representing the start of the expansion as in the Einstein–de Sitter model; E, on the other hand, implies the end of the expansion, or, to use less accurate but more picturesque language, the "end of the world." In the cycloidal universe the world

ends with an inconceivable bang, and we can only congratu-
late ourselves that we shall not be here when it happens. Of
this I am quite confident, because the event E is about 60,000
million years later than S, and more than 50,000 million
years later than now. According to this model, the time
which has elapsed since the initial singular state S is between
5,000 and 6,000 million years, less than the corresponding
period for the Einstein–de Sitter model, and also for the
nonaccelerated model (page 84).

In the cycloidal model, light from distant galaxies is
shifted toward the red while the expansion is going on—that
is to say, during the period SM. During the second half of
the model's history (ME), however, there is a contraction,
and the *red shift becomes a violet shift*. The conditions in
the universe during this period would be very different from
those today. To explain this, let me remind the reader that
the red shift weakens the light from distant galaxies, and it
is this which makes the night sky so dark. If the galaxies
were approaching us, the corresponding violet shift would
strengthen the light, and the night sky would be brighter,
perhaps as bright as the day sky, and this effect would become
intensified as the "end of the world" E approached.

Some cosmologists have argued that conditions during a
contracting phase would be so different from those we know,
that any model requiring such a phase should be ruled out
at once. This view has been put forward by exponents of the
steady-state theory, and I regard it as completely mistaken.
The argument runs as follows: "We live in an expanding
universe, and it is for this sort of universe that we know the
laws of physics. A contracting universe would exhibit certain
important differences, and therefore there is no justification
for carrying over into such a universe the laws as we know
them. Since we do not know what physical laws to use in
contracting models, such models must be ruled out."

In presenting this thesis, the steady-state theorists are, quite understandably, making the most of their own case. One of the features of the steady-state model, as we shall see later, is that the overall picture of the universe remains unchanged. Thus, laws discovered now will always be true because there is no reason for them to be different.

The reason why I am not very much impressed by this argument is that it is part of the everyday business of scientists to extrapolate their laws to a variety of physical conditions, possibly quite different from those in which they have been verified. This is done tentatively, of course, and with a willingness to scrap or alter laws which do not work. Astrophysicists, for example, have no hesitation in applying laws on gases, obtained from laboratory experiments, to the interior of stars where the pressures and temperatures are millions of times greater than those used in the terrestrial work.

I therefore maintain that if the present cosmological observations indicate that we are living in a universe that will one day start to contract, there is no reason for dismay or defeatism. In predicting what the contraction will be like, we must use what scientific laws we now have, and unless there is good reason to the contrary, assume that they are valid alike in the expanding and contracting phases.

According to the cycloidal model, space has a finite volume or is *closed,* as mathematicians say. It is one of the three-dimensional curved spaces which I tried to describe in Chapter 6. The two-dimensional analogue is the surface of a sphere, and if we think of a spherical balloon we can get a very useful picture of a closed expanding model. Imagine a rubber balloon with dots marked on it at equal distances apart, and suppose the balloon is gradually blown up: then every dot will recede from every other dot as the surface of the balloon expands. Here is an illustration of an expanding universe which is finite, and in which every galaxy seems to be at the center and no galaxies are on an edge.

Of course, we have to make the transition from our two-dimensional analogy to three-dimensional curved space, and the skeptic who refuses to do this will just have to accept my word that mathematically a closed three-dimensional curved space is a perfectly valid and well-understood idea. Incidentally, the cycloidal universe begins and ends in a point with no volume, corresponding to the completely deflated balloon.

As in the Einstein–de Sitter model, an observer finds that he can see farther and farther as time passes. However, observation is much more tricky in the cycloidal universe because when the point M is reached (Figure 18) the observer, say O, can just see his antipode, which means that at the extremity of his vision he sees the same object in all directions. (See Figure 19). After M, when the universe begins to shrink, O can see farther than his antipode; therefore he can observe a galaxy at G by either of the routes GAO or GBO. From his point of view this means that he can see the same galaxy by

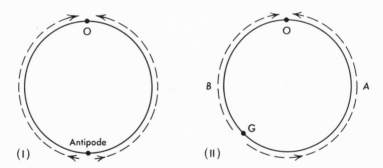

Figure 19. LIGHT-RAYS IN THE CYCLOIDAL MODEL. In (i) the observer O can just see his antipode, which is the point in the universe most distant from him. Rays from his antipode (represented by broken lines) reach him from all directions, and the figure illustrates two of these. The situation at a later time in the universe's history is shown in (ii): rays from a galaxy G can reach O by traveling along either of the paths GAO or GBO.

looking in opposite directions. However, if there were a supernova explosion in that galaxy, O would not see this in both directions because the light from G takes different lengths of time to travel along the two paths: in other words, although O sees the same galaxy G in both directions, he is observing it at different moments in its history. If we allow our imagination to run wild, we can conceive a planet like ours in the galaxy G on which we see a man dying by looking along OAG, and then looking in the opposite direction we can see the same man being born!

As the history of the cycloidal model draws to a close, the point G in Figure 19 moves nearer to O, and finally, at the instant E of the ultimate holocaust, light-rays which left O at the beginning of the expansion complete the journey round the universe and come back to their starting point. Only rays setting off at the very beginning can circumnavigate the universe.

As the model approaches the final annihilation, the light from distant galaxies is shifted very far toward the violet. This increases its energy for precisely similar reasons to those which cause a red shift to weaken the light of a receding source. At the final moment the intensity of light becomes infinite, and the observer faces Olbers's phenomenon in an acute form. This is only one of his worries: others are the infinite density of matter, and the discomfort of living in a universe with zero volume. However, there is no doubt that this absurd situation is a mathematical fiction which arises because we have oversimplified the problem, and then taken too seriously the answer to the oversimplification. More will be said about this in Chapter 8.

Finally, a few words on the cycloid. Consider a wheel which has a point X marked on its rim. Let the wheel roll along a straight line: the curve which X traces out in space is called a cycloid (See Figure 20). It has two sharp points, or

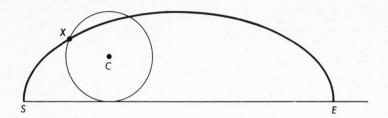

Figure 20. GENERATION OF A CYCLOID. The wheel is represented by the circle, center C. As it rolls along the line SE, the marked point X on its circumference traces out the cycloid. Initially X coincides with S, and as the wheel rolls beyond E, X begins to rise steeply again, generating another cycloidal arch.

cusps, at the ends where the curve rises steeply from the line. In the cosmological model these cusps correspond to the very rapid initial expansion and final contraction.

The cycloid has a distinguished history in applied mathematics because it was found to be the solution of a number of famous problems. One of these was to find the curve of least time, or brachistochrone, defined as follows: take two points at different levels, joined by a smooth wire on which a bead has been threaded; what must be the shape of the wire so that the time taken by the bead to fall from one point to the other is least? The question in itself is not of much physical importance, but the mathematical method needed to solve it leads to the heart of modern theoretical physics. The problem was posed as a challenge to the mathematicians of Europe by the Swiss Jakob Bernoulli in 1696, who probably knew that the answer was a cycloid. No solution was forthcoming for six months. Isaac Newton did not at first hear of the challenge, having grown tired of mathematics and become a conscientious civil servant—to be precise, Master of the Royal Mint. One evening after his day's work, he was told of the problem, and proceeded to solve it between dinner and bedtime!

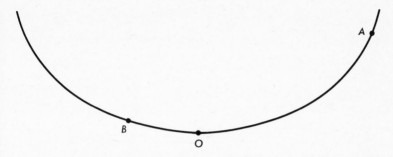

Figure 21. THE TAUTOCHRONE. A smooth wire has the shape of a cycloid. Particles sliding down from A or B reach the base O in equal times.

Another celebrated property of the cycloid is the following. Consider an inverted smooth cycloidal wire (Figure 21), and suppose that a bead slides down it. Then one can show that *the bead always reaches the base* O *in the same time, whatever point it starts from.* For this reason the cycloid is sometimes called the tautochrone (curve of equal time). This seems unbelievable at first, but becomes more credible when one realizes that if the bead starts high up, say, from *A*, it acquires great speed because of the initial steep slope; whereas a bead starting from *B*, although it has not so far to go, makes a very slow start.

The cycloid is an interesting curve in so many ways that a mathematician is not surprised to see it turning up to describe the expansion of the universe. How far this description fits the facts we shall see in Chapter 14.

THE HYPERBOLIC MODEL

There are three relativistic models which stand out because of their mathematical simplicity. Two of these are the Einstein–de Sitter model and the cycloidal one; the third is called the hyperbolic model. The reason for the name is that

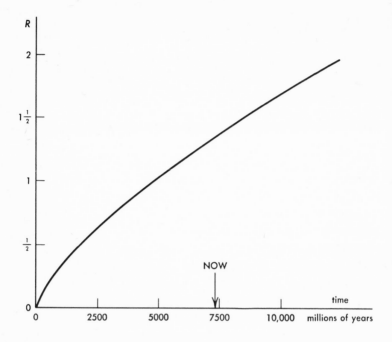

Figure 22. THE HYPERBOLIC MODEL. The function R is taken to have the value unity 5,000 million years after the start of the expansion. The scale is the same as that of the curve for the Einstein–de Sitter model (Figure 17). "Now" indicates that, according to the hyperbolic model, nearly 7,500 million years have elapsed since the singular state.

the space of the model is of an infinite curved type, and the one-dimensional analogue of it is a curve known as the hyperbola (see Figure 23). The hyperbolic model has an expansion curve similar to that of the Einstein–de Sitter model, but it rises rather more steeply (see Figure 22). The curve is not a hyperbola: the reason for calling the model hyperbolic will be explained in the next section. As will be seen from the figure, the model starts from a singular state and expands forever; its volume is infinite.

AN ANALOGY

As I have said before, analogies are dangerous. Why? Suppose we have a complex phenomenon A that has an analogy in terms of a simple one, B. This means that A is like B, but not the same as B. We try to explain how A happens by recalling how B happens. Since we do not properly understand A, we prefer to think in terms of B; the danger is that we may go on doing this after the analogy has broken down, and in this way we get a false picture of A.

I am going to use an analogy to help make the expanding universe more easily comprehensible, but I give warning that since it is an analogy it will break down.

First consider a projectile fired along a tangent to the Earth's surface (note that I write projectile and not rocket), and neglect air resistance. Suppose the velocity is not too large—in fact, less than 6.9 miles per second—so that it returns to Earth. Most people think that its orbit is a parabola: this is not so—the orbit is a part of an ellipse with the center of the Earth as one focus. For practical purposes over small distances the difference is unimportant, but theoretically the distinction is essential. Suppose that the projection velocity is increased: the ellipse becomes more and more cigar-shaped until, when the projection velocity is exactly 6.9, the path becomes a parabola and the projectile does not return to Earth. If the projection velocity is increased still further, the path is a hyperbola, and again the projectile does not come back. (See Figure 23 for illustrations of these curves.) Thus there are three cases:

a) elliptic case: projectile does not escape from the Earth's gravitational field;

b) parabolic case: projectile just escapes;

c) hyperbolic case: projectile escapes.

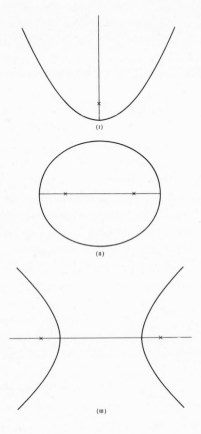

Figure 23. THE CONIC SECTIONS. The curves (i), (ii), and (iii) are the three principal conic sections, the parabola, ellipse, and hyperbola respectively. The straight lines shown are called the axis of the parabola, the major axis of the ellipse, and the transverse axis of the hyperbola. The foci of the curves are marked with crosses. The parabola and hyperbola extend to infinity, but the ellipse is a finite, closed curve. The hyperbola has two separate branches; the path of a projectile, when it is a hyperbola, is confined to one branch.

The parabolic case is a very special one, requiring exactly the right projection speed.

Now suppose that, instead of the Earth and a projectile, we think of two roughly equal bodies (say, two stars) in otherwise empty space. Imagine that, in some way or other, these are projected away from each other. Then, depending on their velocities and their distance apart, they may escape from each other's gravitational field (hyperbolic case), just escape (parabolic case), or not escape (elliptic case). In the elliptic case they would form a binary orbit.

Finally, suppose that a large number of stars, initially near together, are subject to a gigantic explosion. They fly apart, but under the influence of their mutual gravitation. If the explosion is violent enough, so that the initial relative velocities are sufficiently large, the cluster will disintegrate and the stars will fly off in all directions never to return (hyperbolic case). Again, a less violent explosion leading to smaller initial relative velocities will lead to the parabolic limiting case of disintegration; and third, small relative velocities will not enable the stars to escape from their mutual gravitational field, so that after a while gravitation will overcome and reverse the outward velocities, and the cluster will collapse on itself * (elliptic case).

If in the above we now read "galaxies" (or, better, "clusters of galaxies") instead of "stars," we have the promised analogy for the expanding universe. Moreover, the three cases correspond with the three types of model I have described in the previous sections:

Einstein–de Sitter model = parabolic case,

Cycloidal model = elliptic case,

Hyperbolic model = hyperbolic case.

---

* In fact, of course, in an explosion of this nature some stars would gain large velocities and some small, so that some would escape and some not; an ideal case is presented here to simplify the argument.

The two ever-expanding models correspond to the disintegrating clusters, whereas the cycloidal model corresponds to
the case of initial expansion followed by collapse under the
mutual gravitation.

Looked at in this way, the difference among the three
cosmological models is that in the Einstein–de Sitter and the
hyperbolic models the violence of the initial explosion is
sufficient for the mutual gravitation of the galaxies to be
overcome, so that the expansion will go on forever; whereas
in the cycloidal model the initial explosion is not energetic
enough for this to happen.

There is the analogy: now for the snags of which I gave
warning. First, it is not correct to think of the expansion of
the universe as an explosion of particles into *already existing*
empty space. According to relativity, we should think of an
expansion of space itself—here the analogy of the expanding
rubber balloon is better. If the expansion were just an explosion of galaxies into a vast expanse of empty space, there
would be a boundary, and the universe would not be the
same everywhere at the same time, contrary to the cosmological principle. Second, the analogy does not help us to
understand the infinity of galaxies in our two ever-expanding
models, nor does it have anything corresponding to the curvature of space; hence the strange behavior of light-rays in
the cycloidal model has no analogue.

For these reasons the analogy must not be taken too seriously, but it serves to do one useful thing—to illustrate the
effect gravity has on the expanding universe.

OTHER MODELS

Having wrestled with three possible models of the universe, the reader may be surprised and perhaps dismayed to
learn that relativity theory suggests several other models too,

and that these are more complicated than the three described in this chapter. We do not yet know which of our models is the correct one: indeed, the observed data are only accurate enough for us to be able to rule out the more outrageous ones. For the present, cosmologists have to keep open minds on the numerous possibilities. In Chapter 9 I shall give an account of cosmological models which are permitted if one adopts a certain extension of Einstein's field equations, first proposed by him, but which he later disowned. Before turning to these, however, I shall consider in more detail the problem of the singular state in the three simple models, and how far it seems to correspond to the start of the expansion.

8

the start of the expansion

THE EQUATIONS BREAK DOWN

The three models of the universe described in the previous chapter all start from a condition of infinite density which is called a singular state. It is time to ask what this corresponds to in the history of the actual universe.

In mathematical physics we have learned to regard the appearance of infinity in a mathematical expression as a warning that some conception has been stretched beyond its ordinary physical meaning. For example, an important idea in Newton's mechanics is the particle, which is a point having position and also mass, but no volume. The density of the material of the particle must be infinite since

110

$$\text{density} = \frac{\text{mass}}{\text{volume}}$$

and the volume is zero. This infinity serves to remind us that a Newtonian particle has no real existence and is an approximation to bodies, such as billiard balls and planets, whose volumes may be disregarded in certain calculations but which are, of course, not zero.

As long as we clearly understand what we are doing, infinities like this do not matter very much. Unfortunately, in cosmology we have no understanding of what the singular state means. We can see, however, that it presents two distinct problems. The first is the following. At the singular state, the density of matter, and also its pressure, become infinite. All our experience tells us that the state described by these infinite quantities cannot have had a real existence, and that it must be a representation of a condition in which the density and pressure were very high, but finite. Let us therefore assume that the expansion started 10,000 million years ago from a state of high density, and ask what happened in those early times of extreme physical conditions. Had this period any important lasting influence on the chemical composition of the universe? Did it leave traces which we can observe today? This line of research has been extensively treated by George Gamow and his collaborators, and I shall describe their work in the next section.

The second problem presented by the singular state is more fundamental, and even more difficult. It is: What happened before the expansion started? Our model does not tell us because, owing to the appearance of the infinite quantities, Einstein's equations break down altogether at the singular state, and cannot be used to extrapolate the model backward.

It is for this reason that some people refer to the start of the expansion as the creation of the universe. In some unknown way, it is argued, the whole matter of the universe

was created at this moment; there was then a cosmic explosion and the expansion began. We need not try to trace
history back before this event, because the universe, and
indeed, time itself, did not then exist. I shall discuss this idea
later in this chapter.

THE BIG BANG

Physical science usually starts with simple assumptions
and draws complex conclusions. Hence most physicists considering the early history of the expansion have made the
assumption that there first existed only some simple substance, such as hydrogen, and that the chemical complexity
of the universe has arisen later. It is reasonable to assume
this, but only provided you believe that the universe existed
before the expansion started. If you do *not* believe this, the
assumption becomes unnecessary and the problem non-
existent. For if, say, God created the universe 10,000 million
years ago why should He create it out of hydrogen alone?
With small extra trouble He could presumably have made
the other elements too in their correct abundances, and saved
us the trouble of explaining their formation.

The start of the expansion is colloquially referred to as the
"big bang." The most ambitious and detailed theory of the big
bang is that of Gamow and collaborators, known as the
$\alpha \, \beta \, \gamma$ theory because the main memoir describing it bore
the names Alpher, Bethe, and Gamow. They assume that the
universe started as a very dense, hot mass of neutrons. These
soon decayed to form protons and electrons, but some of the
first protons joined with the neutrons still remaining to produce atomic nuclei of various stages of complexity. The temperature while this was happening was about 10,000 million
degrees, and most of the heavy elements were built up in the
first 30 minutes of the expansion!

This was the $\alpha \beta \gamma$ theory, at least in general outline; but unfortunately, when Gamow and his collaborators got down to detailed calculations they met a snag that proved insuperable. The hydrogen nucleus consists of one proton, so hydrogen nuclei were formed directly from the decay of neutrons; the next heavier atom is helium whose nucleus contains two neutrons and two protons, and the theory showed how this could have formed. After helium the next atom is lithium with a nucleus containing four neutrons and three protons, and the theory had to show how this could be built up from helium step by step, through intermediate nuclei containing five and six nuclear particles (nucleons). However, a collection of five nucleons is unstable, and if such a complex had formed, it would at once have broken down into helium again. The only hope for getting something more complex would be for a helium nucleus to be hit simultaneously by two particles which might produce a stable complex of six nucleons: however, this is a rather unlikely event, and in the conditions then prevailing would not have happened often enough to overcome the difficulty.

It therefore appears that although the neutrons could have produced the hydrogen and helium—of which together, incidentally, the universe is probably more than 99 percent composed—they could not have produced the heavier elements. So the $\alpha \beta \gamma$ theory fails to achieve its purpose.

An alternative view of the initial explosion was given by the Belgian, Abbé Georges Lemaître, in connection with a cosmological model advocated by him and described in the next chapter. Instead of supposing that the universe began with simplicity and developed complexity, Lemaître starts from one extremely complex object—a primeval atom, as he calls it. This must not be pictured as an atom such as we know it, because it contained all the matter of the universe.

It was extremely unstable, and no sooner had it come into existence than it disintegrated into millions of pieces. This disintegration was similar to, but very much more complicated than, radioactive disintegrations of uranium, radium, and so on. Among the decay products were the atoms we know, and also much more complex atoms which have long since disappeared because they have disintegrated into simpler ones.

Uranium decays into helium and lead, and during the process certain radiations are emitted—namely, X rays and β-rays (electrons)—and also charged particles, called α-particles, which are helium nuclei. These emissions contain energy, and it is this energy which is responsible for the damage caused by an atomic fission bomb. Lemaître supposes that in the disintegration of the primeval atom the accompanying emission of radiation and particles would have been extremely powerful; so powerful, in fact, that traces of it would still be found traveling about in the universe. Now, it happens that physicists do observe a type of emission which could be the vestigial remains of Lemaître's primeval atomic explosion. This is called *cosmic radiation*.

Cosmic radiation falls steadily on the Earth from outer space, roughly the same amount coming from every direction. It is not radiation in quite the ordinary sense, because when it enters the Earth's atmosphere it consists largely of protons and α-particles, with some heavier atomic nuclei such as carbon and oxygen. These particles collide with atoms in the atmosphere, and numerous different nuclear products then result.

No completely satisfactory theory of cosmic rays has been suggested. Experts nowadays incline to the view that they are not really cosmic at all, but come from neighboring galaxies. According to one theory, vast reservoirs of charged particles reside between the stars, kept in equilibrium by the magnetic fields of the galaxies. Cosmic rays consist of those particles which gradually seep out of the reservoir.

There is no compelling reason for believing Lemaître's theory, because, unlike Gamow, he has not worked out the details of the disintegration process to find whether it really can account for the abundances of the different types of atom. The evidence, in any case, suggests that evolution since the start of the expansion has been a building up of complex material from simpler atoms such as hydrogen, rather than a process of decomposition. And the really big question is, of course: How could a huge atom like this form, and where did it come from?

WAS THERE REALLY A BIG BANG?

We have seen that neither the fusion-bomb theory of Gamow nor the primeval fission-bomb of Lemaître is successful in accounting for the origin and abundances of the heavy elements. Since these elements certainly exist, there seem to be three possible ways to proceed. First, we might make further attempts to construct a theory on the lines of Gamow or Lemaître; second, to anyone who believes that the universe was created 10,000 million years ago there is, as we have seen, no problem, because to the major miracle of creation one might as well add the minor miracle that some elements were created heavier than others; third, we may look for some other process by which the heavy elements have been created.

The first course of action does not seem hopeful in view of the failure of the previous determined attempts, especially that of Gamow; the second does not recommend itself to any scientific person; and it is the third that has been tried and has completely solved the problem.

The chemical factory we are looking for turns out to be in the interior of the stars. This was suspected about ten years ago when the spectrum of an element called technetium was noticed in certain stars. Why this was significant is that technetium suffers fairly rapid radioactivity decay, and had it been created at the big bang it would have disintegrated long ago. The fact that it is observed now suggests that its formation must be going on at the present time.

Subsequently, patient efforts by astrophysicists, especially Hoyle, have given a theoretical backing to the generation of heavy elements in stars. It will be remembered that stars shine because they convert hydrogen into helium, and energy is given out in the process. In some stars, called red giants, the helium can be converted in a step-by-step process to carbon, whose mass is twelve times that of hydrogen, and thence to still heavier elements.* It is now generally agreed that the stars are sufficiently effective producers of the heavier elements to account for the observed abundances.

It follows that the big bang is not required to account for the production of heavy elements. It was this function which originally attracted cosmologists to the models with an initial singular state, because at that time the big bang seemed the only way of explaining atomic abundances. Now that the alternative explanation is available, we can drop the idea of a big bang provided our cosmological models can be altered so that they have no singular state. The ones described in the last chapter all have such a state, but in the next section but one, and in Chapters 9 and 10, I shall describe other relativistic models which have no singular state.

---

* It will be remembered that the $\alpha\beta\gamma$ theory failed because it could not explain how atoms containing more than five nucleons were synthesized in the early stages of the cosmic expansion. The difficulty is that, since the nucleus containing five nucleons is unstable, a helium nucleus has to be hit simultaneously by two particles; and because the density is not very high, such an event can happen only very rarely. With the much higher densities prevailing in giant stars, this collision process occurs much more frequently, and sufficient nuclei containing six nucleons are formed for the synthesis to proceed.

A JOB FOR GOD?

I have already mentioned the view that the start of the expansion is to be identified with the creation of the universe. This idea I regard as mistaken and thoroughly unscientific. It asserts that the start of the expansion is not a scientific problem, whereas I believe that *all* genuine problems are scientific ones in the sense that they can be subjected to scientific method and analysis. The danger of the idea has already been referred to: that it would relieve us of the need to explain how the heavy elements have been formed, because if we accept it, we might as well say they turned up all in their correct proportions at the creation. Similarly, there is no need to explain how the galaxies formed from the primeval hydrogen, because they too could have been present at the creation.

The underlying motive is, of course, to bring in God as creator. It seems like the opportunity Christian theology has been waiting for ever since science began to depose religion from the minds of rational men in the seventeenth century. The first serious blow to the theologians was when Copernicus suggested that the Sun and not the Earth was the center of the universe. Galileo, who amplified and taught Copernicus' views in Italy, was forced by the Roman Catholic Church to recant. But the dogmatism of the Church could not stop the new knowledge, and the splendor of Newton's theory of mechanics brought universal recognition, first, that Copernicus had been right, and second, that the laws of mechanics could be mastered by man's intellect, without theological assistance. There is a story of how Laplace, the famous French mathematical physicist, showed Napoleon his book on celestial mechanics in which he worked out in detail the motions of the planets. Napoleon remarked, "You have written this huge book on the system of the world without once mentioning the author of the universe." "Sire," replied Laplace, "I had no need of that hypothesis."

God having been excluded from mechanics, and later from the rest of physics, the theologians retreated to what was then the backwoods of knowledge. "Very well," they said, "although physical phenomena can be explained entirely by reason, this concerns mere material objects. It is entirely different with living matter: this contains a vital principle which comes from God. Science will never be able to deal with living things." This attitude has a long history in the biological sciences. It was even thought that chemicals like fats and sugar which come from living matter are in some qualitative way different from those like salt and water which occur in the inanimate world. Hence the names organic and inorganic chemicals, which we still use. This difference was shown to be illusory when in 1828 Wöhler synthesized urea (which occurs in urine) from inorganic materials.

Gradually it has been recognized that biology is as much a science as physics; but there still exist some vitalists who believe that there is a mystic principle which will forever prevent scientists from creating living matter in the laboratory. However, during the nineteenth century, Christian theologians put forward a new argument. Even if science could understand animals, they said, it would never be possible to be scientific about human beings because they have a soul, specially created by God. It was for this reason that Darwin's theory of evolution was such a bitter blow to theology and was fought with such tenacity: for here was a theory asserting that men and apes have common ancestors, thereby denying men any special place in the world of living creatures. In this battle, as in the others, science was victorious.

During the twentieth century the last bastion of dogmatic

reaction has become the study of the human mind, and die-hard theologians maintain that this at least is forever immune to the probings of science. Past experience, as well as progress in psychology, gives us every reason to suppose that this view is as false as its predecessors.

The situation being as black as this, one can well understand the enthusiasm with which some theologians accepted the idea that the universe was created 10,000 million years ago. Here was the vacancy for God which they had been seeking. Archbishop Ussher had been a few years wrong with the date, but he had the right idea when he said that God created the world in 4004 B.C.

Unfortunately, some cosmologists have been sympathetic to this attitude. This seems to me quite reprehensible for the following reason. It is the business of science to offer rational explanations for all the events in the real world, and any scientist who calls on God to explain something is falling down on his job. This applies as much to the start of the expansion as to any other event. If the explanation is not forthcoming at once, the scientist must suspend judgment: but if he is worth his salt he will always maintain that a rational explanation will eventually be found. This is the one piece of dogmatism that a scientist can allow himself—and without it science would be in danger of giving way to superstition every time that a problem defied solution for a few years.

Let me repeat that the singular state at the start of the expansion means that certain quantities in our mathematical equations become infinite. Our models of the universe therefore break down, and what we must do is to correct them. There has been a curious reluctance on the part of the cosmologists I mentioned to do this, and they have preferred to identify the singularity in the equations with God. Now, I argue that scientifically this is inexcusable, but I should have thought that theologically it is very dangerous, because if God is brought in just to patch up our mathematics then He may become redundant when better mathematics is discovered.

Theologians enter this subject at their own risk, but for scientists the task is surely clear enough. We must try to find a rational cause for the start of the expansion, and to push our knowledge back beyond the phony singular state to the previous epoch of the universe.

BEFORE THE EXPANSION—WHAT?

Let us agree that the singular state is a mathematical fiction and that the start of the expansion had a rational cause. We believe that it happened about 10,000 million years ago, so evidence will not be easy to find. Moreover, if there was a period of intense temperature and pressure, any relics of a previous epoch in the universe's history are likely to have been vaporized into their ultimate nuclear constituents. Clearly, our task of finding out why the expansion started is going to be difficult. Nevertheless, let us start by considering a theory that will give us some idea what to look for.

It will be recalled that in the cycloidal model the expansion is followed by a contraction which ends in a singular state. What if, instead of this singular state, the contraction should be the prelude to another expanding phase? Then the cycle of expansion and contraction could go on forever, and the universe would have an indefinite past and future: its history would be a never-ending series of oscillations. Let us consider how this looks in terms of the scale function R which represents the distance between two typical galaxies. The graph of R against time would be like the curve shown in Figure 24. Instead of the cusps at S and E in Figure 18, there are now smooth curves at the minima A, B, . . . representing a gradual transition from contraction to expansion. In

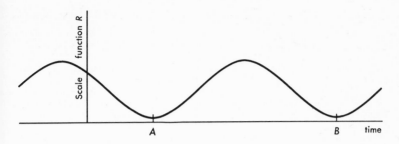

Figure 24. AN OSCILLATING MODEL. Each contracting period in the universe's history ends in a smooth transition to the subsequent period of expansion. There are no singular states.

this model the singular state is abolished, and at the start of each expanding phase we should have a state of high, but not infinite, density and pressure.

The question we have to answer, though, is what can have made the contraction slow down, cease, and change to expansion. In terms of the analogy of Chapter 7, we ask why the collapsing cluster of stars should slow down, stop, and then fly outward again.

At present we have no answer: no physical mechanism which would reverse the contraction has yet been discovered. One would guess that the reversal must be due to some elastic properties of the cosmic medium: in the analogy, we may imagine the contracting cluster bouncing out against a resistance. Indeed, a mechanism for the reversal seems obvious at first: in the contraction the gases of the universe get pent up to such an extent that finally the outward pressure forces them to expand again. Such a process is believed to cause the oscillation of a star such as a Cepheid.

Unfortunately, this explanation will not work. In the final stages of the contraction the temperature becomes so high that matter is split up into its constituent nucleons, and all these are homogeneously distributed. Because of this homo-

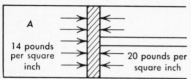

Figure 25. MOTION OF A PISTON. The pressure of the gas in the chamber A is 14 pounds per square inch, and the pressure on the other side is 20 pounds per square inch. The difference in pressure makes the piston move.

geneity the pressure is the same everywhere—or to put it another way, there are no *pressure differences* anywhere. Now, it is pressure differences which cause objects to move—for example, the piston in Figure 25, which compresses the gas in the chamber A because of the pressure difference of six pounds per square inch. It is a pressure difference that we need to reverse the expansion as suggested in the previous paragraph: and this we do not have.

This is not quite the last word on the effect of pressure. According to classical physics, all that matters is the pressure difference. Thus in Figure 25 if the pressure difference were zero, it would not matter whether the pressures on the two sides were both 20 pounds or both 200 pounds per square inch; there would be no mechanical distinction whatever in the two cases. But general relativity says that pressure has a certain effect on a body in its own right—even if there is no pressure difference. This is a very queer effect, and very hard to picture. A positive pressure exerts an attraction, whereas a negative pressure (that is, a tension) exerts a repulsion. It is a repulsion that we need to reverse the contraction and start the next expansion. Now, although some substances, such as steel, can sustain tensions, gases as far as we know always exert a positive pressure, so it is hard to see how we can get a negative pressure from the cosmic medium. But we have to remember that if the temperature is several thousands of millions of degrees, matter may show quite unexpected properties. Near the minimum points of Figure 24, when it consists of a gas of nuclear particles, matter may possibly be able to support a negative pressure, and this may be enough to reverse the contraction.

This is rather conjectural, but at least it gives us a scientific idea to work on in our search for an explanation of the singular state. Whether it is right or not we may hope to find out when we know more about the behavior of matter under extreme conditions, either from our studies of stars or by the extrapolation of theoretical results learned from laboratory work.

Incidentally, we know that the conditions before the start of the expansion must have been severe for the following reason: The universe now is mainly hydrogen, but hydrogen burns up in stars to form helium, and eventually there will be no hydrogen left. If the cycloidal model is correct, the hydrogen will have burned out before the next minimum of the curve, so if the cycle is to repeat itself fresh hydrogen must be generated somehow.

From the predominance of hydrogen today we deduce that there must have been a rejuvenation fairly recently. This must have happened at the minimum and certainly required very high temperatures.

If the universe has passed through a minimum of the expansion curve—that is, through a state of maximum density —it may soon be possible to verify this from observations on distant galaxies. It will be recalled that the farther we look out into space, the farther we look back into time. This is because light from distant galaxies has been on its journey for a long time, and we see them as they were when the light was emitted. If, therefore, we can look out far enough, we may be able to see through the minimum into the contracting phase.* At these great distances, the red shift would then become a violet shift because the galaxies there would be

* Provided there are no difficulties with horizons: in the model shown in Figure 24 these would not arise, but they might in certain others.

approaching and not receding. There should also be a maximum in the number of galaxies per unit volume, corresponding to the maximum density, at a certain distance from the Milky Way; this might be detectable in the radio observations. We know that we are not seeing far enough yet, either with optical or radio instruments, but we may be able to before too long.

SUMMARY OF CHAPTER 8

In this chapter I have been considering the singular state occurring in the three relativistic models of Chapter 7. I have argued that this arises because the models break down when extrapolated too far into the past. This does not mean that they are inadequate to describe the present state of the universe; but they become unsatisfactory if applied when the density was very high. We need not feel surprised that the same highly simplified mathematical models do not apply both now and also when the density was 10^{30} times higher!

At present we do not know how to alter the simple models to take account of the conditions of high density. I maintain, nevertheless, that the problem is a scientific one. To illustrate how it might be solved, I have suggested, tentatively, an oscillating model, similar to the cycloidal one in its contemporary behavior but very different in the remote past and future.

In the following chapters, other models without singular states will be described.

9

relativistic models
with cosmic repulsion

EVEN EINSTEIN WAS FALLIBLE

The general theory of relativity appeared in 1915, and
K. Schwarzschild in 1916 produced the first exact solution of
the field equations, referring to the gravitational field of the
Sun. Einstein himself was soon engaged in the task of
applying general relativity to the universe as a whole. At that
time it was thought that except for minor local motions the
universe must be static, so Einstein naturally sought a static
solution of his field equations. He found none. It looked as
if general relativity did not apply to the universe as a whole.

Einstein therefore modified his original field equations by the addition of a certain term, known as the lambda term after the Greek letter λ which was used to denote it in the formulae. The modification had to be such that the harmony of the original theory with astronomical facts of the solar system was not disturbed. This condition was satisfied by the λ-term, which has negligible effect on the gravitational field over small distances (such as the diameter of the solar system, or even the Milky Way), but which over distances of cosmological dimensions has an important influence.

The modified form of the field equations gave Einstein what he wanted—a model of a static universe. This is called the Einstein universe (not to be confused with the Einstein–de Sitter universe of Chapter 7), and was the first cosmological model.

In the same year 1917, de Sitter took the modified field equations and found a very remarkable solution of them. The details of de Sitter's solution will be described later, but it can be stated here that the solution referred to an empty universe which is nevertheless expanding—in the sense that if a small particle is introduced, it will recede from the observer just as galaxies do.

Here was the first definite indication that the universe might be expanding. It must be emphasized that the model appeared several years before observations showed clearly that there is a general recession of the galaxies. Although Slipher had started measuring galactic red shifts in 1912, astronomers were puzzled, as explained in Chapter 5, by the number of violet shifts, and as late as 1922 Eddington was doubtful whether the recession was general.

It can fairly be claimed that general relativity here made a theoretical prediction of the greatest importance. This is what a good theory ought to do—to tell observers what to look for, instead of being wise after the event, and presenting the explanation after the observations have been made.

It was, in fact, the second scoop for general relativity. The first was a result of Schwarzschild's solution of Einstein's equations, which predicted that rays of light are bent by a gravitational field. If rays from a distant star pass close to the Sun, they are deflected and the star is seen in a slightly displaced position (see Figure 26). Rays of light should be bent according to Newton's theory also, but only by half the amount required by relativity.

Astronomers soon realized that here was the chance of a clear-cut decision between the old theory of gravitation and the new. A committee of the Royal Society and the Royal

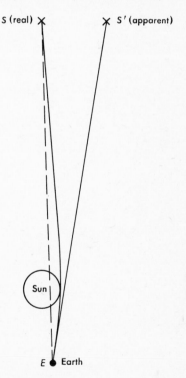

Figure 26. THE BENDING OF LIGHT. The path of light from a distant star, S, is bent by the Sun's gravitational field as shown. To a terrestrial observer, if he assumes that light-rays travel in straight lines, the star appears to be in position S'. If the Sun were not in the way, the light from S would travel on the broken line SE. General relativity gives correctly the angle SES' between the true and apparent directions of the star.

Stars such as S that lie in the Sun's direction can be seen only when the Sun is totally eclipsed by the Moon, and observations of the bending of light are made during total eclipses. The true direction of S is found by observations six months later, when the Earth is on the other side of the Sun, so that the starlight does not pass through the Sun's gravitational field before reaching the Earth.

S (real)   S' (apparent)

Sun

E Earth

Astronomical Society, both of London, set about arranging expeditions to observe the next eclipse of the Sun, which was in May, 1919. One expedition went to Brazil and the other to North Africa: the results of the observations were a clear validation of relativity. Newton's theory, supreme for two hundred and fifty years, had now to give way. The philosopher A. N. Whitehead, who was present at the meeting of the Royal Society at which the Astronomer Royal announced that Einstein's prediction had been verified, described the scene as follows: "The whole atmosphere of tense interest was exactly that of the Greek drama: we were the chorus commenting on the decree of destiny as disclosed in the development of a supreme incident. There was dramatic quality in the very staging—the traditional ceremonial, and in the background the picture of Newton to remind us that the greatest of scientific generalizations was now, after more than two centuries, to receive its first modification. Nor was the personal interest wanting: a great adventure in thought had at length come safe to shore."

Let us return to de Sitter's solution of Einstein's equations. It is clear that to Einstein, de Sitter's discovery must have come as a shock, and it was one of the reasons which later impelled him to abandon the λ-term, and to revert to the original field equations. It seems that Einstein had previously looked for the solution de Sitter found, but had missed it. Had he found it, Einstein would probably never have put forward the modified theory (though certainly somebody else would have done so later on).

Einstein's distaste for de Sitter's solution arose because he profoundly disliked the idea of a universe which is empty, yet nevertheless contains fields of force. (That such fields exist in de Sitter's model follows from the motion of the small test particles.) Fields of force, Einstein thought, cannot exist without matter, so he firmly rejected as unrealistic de

Sitter's model, and with it the λ-term which had given rise to it.

An important development took place in 1922 when the German mathematician Friedmann discovered the three expanding models described in Chapter 7. As stated there, these satisfy the unmodified equations; they therefore demonstrate that expanding models can be obtained without the λ-term. Shortly after Friedmann's discovery, astronomers began to realize that the universe is expanding, and there seemed to Einstein and many others no reason to retain the λ, or cosmological, term in the field equations. It will be recalled that the term had been introduced to obtain a *static* model of the universe, which was now ruled out by observation.

Nevertheless, many cosmologists have investigated models which arise only when the λ-term is retained. Some of these are of great interest, and two outstanding cosmologists, Eddington and Lemaître, have stanchly maintained that the cosmological term must be kept in the field equations. Their models will be described in the following sections.

From the mathematical point of view, the addition to the field equations of the λ-term enormously complicates our problems. As I have explained before, the main way in which we theorists make progress is to find solutions of the field equations. These are hard enough to find even with the equations in their unmodified form; but with the λ-term, the problem becomes preposterously difficult. I should explain that if the λ-term is to be introduced into cosmology, then it will have to be put into the field equations of general relativity too. In the past few years a tremendous amount of work has been done in general relativity finding solutions corresponding to gravitational waves. All this work has used the unmodified field equations, and nearly all of it will have to be scrapped if we are forced to adopt the λ-term.

This is why most of us hope that the cosmological problem can be solved without using the λ-term. On grounds of simplicity, we might expect the unmodified equations to be correct: as Einstein used to say, "God is subtle but not malicious."* Of course, this is an expression of faith, but like all scientific beliefs it is subject to disproof by observation. As soon as the astronomers show conclusively that none of the three simple models of Chapter 7 will fit the observations, we theorists promise to give the λ-term a hearty welcome!

Let me now give the reader some indications of the variety and complexity which result when the modified equations are allowed.

THE EINSTEIN UNIVERSE

This, the first cosmological model, is completely static. The space in it is curved, with a finite volume, and its two-dimensional analogue is the surface of a sphere. A ray of light could travel completely round the Einstein universe and return to its starting point in about 10,000 million years.

What precisely is meant by the static condition of the model is not clear. A universe of stars at rest, even if one were possible, would not be unchanging (and therefore not static) because the stars are continually radiating energy. Perhaps the model refers to a completely uniform mass of gas, say hydrogen.

In 1930 Eddington showed that the Einstein model is unstable. This means that if a small disturbance takes place in the model it will grow, and the whole universe will either contract or expand. Now a universe in which no small motion whatever can occur is unthinkable, unless one stretches one's imagination to contemplate a model full of gas everywhere at the absolute zero of temperature (at which no motion is pos-

---

* Einstein was an agnostic, but he used "God" as a synonym for "nature."

sible). Excluding this farfetched and uninteresting case, we are forced to conclude that Einstein's universe must eventually change into an expanding or contracting one.

WHAT DOES THE λ–TERM MEAN?

The Einstein model gives us a clue to the physical meaning of the λ-term. Why should a static universe be possible with a λ-term, but not without? The reason is that the unmodified equations describe pure gravitation, and we should not therefore expect a static model to exist, because all the matter would collapse under its own gravitational field. Why does the λ-term prevent the collapse? Because it represents a force of repulsion which counteracts gravitation and keeps the model in equilibrium.

The force is of a very unusual kind. Forces of repulsion are well known in physics—for example, in electricity two positive, charged particles repel each other with a force proportional to the product of the charges, and inversely proportional to the square of their distance apart. Such a force depends on some specific property of the matter—in this example, the electric charge. It also decreases as the distance between the particles increases. But the cosmic repulsion is such that from any point O in the universe, matter is repelled with a force proportional to its distance from O. Thus, the *greater the distance, the greater the repulsion.* The repulsive force on a galaxy is proportional to the mass of the galaxy itself, but quite independent of the mass of the galaxy at O, or indeed of whether there is a galaxy at O at all.

This idea, that galaxies have a greater effect on each other the farther they are away, is very strange to most of us who have been brought up to believe that things interact more strongly the closer they are. It is clear now why the λ-term is important only in cosmology: because over short distances, such as those in our own galaxy, the repulsion is very small, but over cosmological distances it becomes appreciable.

We can now formulate a physical explanation of why the Einstein universe is unstable. In its undisturbed condition, gravitational attraction and cosmic repulsion just balance. Now, suppose that for some unknown reason a part of the universe becomes rarefied: the rarefaction means that the distances between the galaxies are increased, which implies that the gravitation is weakened and the cosmic repulsion strengthened. The latter force on the galaxies concerned now favors expansion, and the weaker gravity has not enough power to stop it. Thus a part of the universe starts to expand, and this will presumably be enough to start a general expansion. A similar argument shows that an initial condensation will start a contraction, since if this happens the enhanced gravitational attraction becomes the unbalanced force.

When during the 1920's the expansion of the universe first became established, astronomers naturally believed that it was connected with the cosmic repulsion introduced into the field equations by the λ-term. It was only later when Friedmann's work became understood that it was realized that expanding models were possible without the λ-term (namely, the big bang models described in Chapter 7). The effect of retaining the λ-term is to increase the expansion rate, as we shall see shortly.

EDDINGTON'S MODEL

Eddington followed his discovery that the Einstein model is unstable by the suggestion that the universe as we know it started from a disturbance of the Einstein state. He proposed a model in which the graph of the expansion function R against the time is as shown in Figure 27. After an infinite length of time in the static Einstein state, the universe suffers

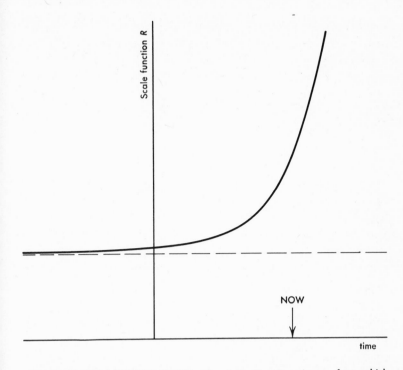

Figure 27. EDDINGTON'S MODEL. The static Einstein universe, from which Eddington's model originates, is represented by the broken line. The expansion is initially very slow, but later becomes extremely rapid.

the fatal disturbance, and starts expanding, very slowly at first, but afterward with an increasing speed. According to Eddington's model, the expansion has perhaps been in progress for 10,000 million years, but may have been going on for much longer. Actually, there is no known reason why the static Einstein model should have started expanding rather than contracting, but Eddington's attention was naturally focused on the expanding case.

The main difference between Eddington's model and the two ever-expanding models of Chapter 7 is, of course, the absence of the singular state. It was for this reason that the model did not meet with much support in the 1930's, because without a singular state there seemed to be no means whereby the heavy elements could form. Eddington himself believed that this was not a valid criticism, because he thought that these elements could form in stars. In this he has been completely vindicated by recent work. Another apparent difficulty was that, since the universe had an infinite past, the hydrogen which it presumably contained to start with must all have been burned up long ago, in contradiction with the observed fact that there is still a great deal of hydrogen in the universe. However, this criticism too can be overcome if one supposes that the stars did not begin to form until after the primeval gas had started to expand.

Eddington associated his model with an ambitious program intended to explain the whole of physics. He was greatly impressed by the common occurrence of certain very large numbers,* which is quite unexplained by orthodox theory but which he felt could not be the result of chance. To explain these coincidences, he devised a theory which purported to unify general relativity and atomic theory, a task which has been persistently and unsuccessfully attempted by physicists, including Einstein, ever since 1915. The consensus of opinion is that Eddington's attempt was a failure. The more charitable of his critics pointed out that the theory accounted only for already known results, and predicted nothing new; the less kindly said that he was mystic, and even that he cooked his results.

Eddington, like E. A. Milne, another famous British

---

* For example, the ratio

$$\frac{\text{Electric force between proton and electron}}{\text{Gravitational force between proton and electron}} = 2 \times 10^{39}$$

is independent of the units in which the forces are expressed, and approximately the same number turns up in the ratio of other quite different physical quantities.

cosmologist of the interwar years, was what philosophers call a rationalist. He believed that by sitting down and thinking, a man should, if clever enough, be able to deduce the laws of nature. His ideas on this subject were fascinating, but he did not prove his point. Rationalists nowadays are less popular than empiricists, who believe that we have to go out and examine the world in order to find out what nature is like. It remains to be shown whether rationalism can produce new and fruitful scientific results.

To revert to Eddington's cosmological model, it seems to me that, from the philosophical point of view, the absence of a singular state is a considerable advantage, for the reasons explained in the last chapter. On the other hand, the Eddington model cannot exist without the λ-term which most of us would like to abolish. It also suffers from the disadvantage that one can hardly take seriously the infinite period before the disturbance because, unless matter was at the absolute zero of temperature, there would have been some motion which would have set off instability; and if matter had really been at absolute zero it is not clear how instability could *ever* have developed.

As already stated, Eddington in 1930 discovered the instability of the Einstein universe, and thereafter advocated the cosmological model I have denoted by his name. This model had already been announced by Lemaître in 1927 in a rather obscure journal, and it was only when Eddington came across Lemaître's work in 1930 and subsequently publicized it that it became generally known. Indeed, one is struck by the disinclination of cosmologists of this period to read anybody's work except their own! The big bang models of Chapter 7 had been discovered by Friedmann in 1922, but his work lay neglected until the early 1930's; and there seemed to be ignorance in Europe of work by American cosmologists. I am glad to say that nowadays we are less egocentric, and do take notice of what other cosmologists discover.

THE DE SITTER MODEL

De Sitter's was the first expanding cosmological model, but, as I explained previously, it is a model with the very strange property of being empty. We say that it is expanding because we know from calculations, using general relativity, that if a small particle were introduced into it, this would, if allowed to move freely, recede from the observer (who also is supposed to move freely, that is, not under the influence of forces or rockets). This may seem a slightly doubtful reason for calling the model an expanding one, but it is in accordance with standard practice in relativity. When we have derived a solution of the field equations, we examine its properties by finding out what would happen to a small particle introduced into the field (called a *test* particle). For example, in the case of Schwarzschild's solution for the Sun's gravitational field, we find by calculation that test particles should describe elliptical orbits, the major axes of which slowly rotate in their own plane. We can regard the planets as test particles compared with the Sun's enormous mass, so we can verify our calculations by observing the planetary orbits.

One very remarkable thing about the de Sitter model is that there is no definite answer to the question whether or not space is curved: it depends on the motion of the observer who is looking at it. Even stranger is the fact that the observers to whom space is curved find it finite in volume; whereas those to whom it is flat find that it is infinite!

These seemingly incredible properties of the de Sitter model stem from a feature of relativity which I have mentioned briefly before—that the three dimensions of space and one of time have to be treated together as a four-dimensional continuum. This four-dimensional structure is the ultimate reality, but our mode of perception makes us split it into three spatial dimensions and one of time. It was previously thought that there was only one way of doing this splitting, but relativity has shown that there is an infinity of ways, depending on how the percipient happens to be moving and how he chooses his frame of reference. This is the cause of a well-known result of special relativity, that absolute simultaneity does not exist—which means that two events simultaneous for one observer are not necessarily simultaneous for another. In the de Sitter universe, the consequences of the choice of frame of reference can be so important that different observers would not even agree on whether space is infinite—mainly because by "space" they would mean different things. Because of the theory of relativity, however, there is no real conflict between their observations, only an apparent one. If the observers understand general relativity they can easily reconcile their results and convince themselves that they are just seeing different aspects of the same thing.

Another related oddity of the de Sitter model is that one cannot say definitely whether it is static or not. To some observers (in fact, the ones who see its space as finite) it looks static, whereas to others it looks almost as dynamic as one of the big bang models. Mathematicians prefer to call the de Sitter model stationary, which means that although there is change, the overall picture is unaltered. I shall describe this property in more detail later.

I will not write further now on the de Sitter universe for the following reason: The model was important, as I have already explained, in providing an initial forecast of the expansion. With the discovery of expanding models containing matter, the empty de Sitter model was no longer considered of practical interest, although it has always had great curiosity value. Then in 1948 when Bondi, Gold, and Hoyle

were looking for a world model which would give a greater
"age of the universe" than that given by the big bang models,
they took over the de Sitter universe, modified it, and called
the result the steady-state model. Because I shall be describing
the theory of this model at length in Chapter 12, further
study of the de Sitter model can wait till then.

LEMAÎTRE'S MODEL

As already explained, Lemaître's first cosmological model
was the one I have called the Eddington model because
Eddington advocated it wholeheartedly throughout his later
years, and built a far-reaching theory of atomic physics on it.
The model which Lemaître ultimately came to believe in was
different in many respects, although both models have in
common the use of the λ-term.

The graph of the scale function R for Lemaître's model
is shown in Figure 28. The model starts from a singular state
at O, and begins to expand rapidly. Later the expansion
slows down, and for a period, represented in the diagram by
AB, there is hardly any expansion at all. After this, the
expansion speeds up again and continues at an ever-increasing rate.

Lemaître's model shows very clearly the effect of the
λ-term. It starts with a big bang, and the initial rapid expansion is similar to that at the beginning of the models of
Chapter 7, in which λ is absent. At this stage the expansion,
though rapid, is being slowed down by gravitation. Then
follows, as it were, a battle between gravitational attraction
and cosmic repulsion during the period AB, when R is almost
stationary. Eventually, the repulsion wins, and subsequently
gravitation is not of much importance because the galaxies
have by that time separated to great distances; the final
period in the history of the model is represented by an ever-

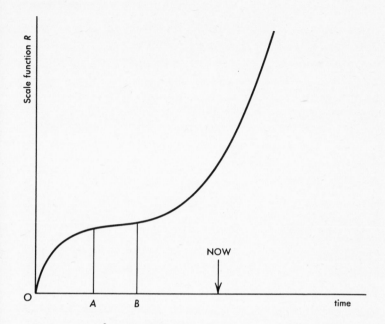

Figure 28. LEMAÎTRE'S MODEL. The start of the expansion resembles that in the cycloidal model. It is followed by an almost static period, but eventually the model expands very rapidly.

lasting expansion under the influence of the λ-term alone, and is increasingly rapid. Were it not for the cosmic repulsion, this model would be similar to the cycloidal one and would collapse back on itself between *A* and *B*. Like the cycloidal model, Lemaître's has curved space and a finite volume.

The model has several advantages over the simple big bang models of Chapter 7. Because it is more flexible than the latter models, there is no need for a panic every time observational astronomers change their minds about the "age of the universe." This flexibility arises because the value of λ is not yet known with accuracy, so it can be adjusted to make the period *AB* as long as required. The period *AB* is also useful in that it permits galaxies to form out of the primeval gas. The formation of galaxies is hard to account for on the simple big bang models, as will be explained in Chapter 12.

Lemaître's universe exhibits a very interesting horizon. It will be remembered that in the models of Chapter 7 an observer could see farther and farther as time passed. The same is true of the Lemaître model during the initial period OA, but afterward, and especially after B, the observer's knowledge of the universe becomes less complete as time passes. After B, there are events in the universe which the observer will never be able to see, even if he waits an infinite time for the information to come to him, or even if he leaves his galaxy and travels in search of it. Since the space of the model is *finite*, this is surprising, because one might think that as the light from the event has only a finite distance to cover, it must eventually reach the observer. What happens, though, is that owing to the cosmic repulsion the expansion becomes so rapid that light emitted from a very distant event cannot travel fast enough to cover the increasing distance. As Fred Hoyle has remarked, it is a case of taking "all the running you can do, to keep in the same place," as the Red Queen said to Alice in *Through the Looking-Glass*.

Still stranger features of this horizon are to come. The observer never sees any galaxy cross it—if he sees a galaxy once he will always be able to see it. One may ask, since the galaxy is receding, surely it must cross any finite horizon? The answer is that it *does* cross the horizon, but the observer continues to receive the light which it emits before it crosses; he will never receive any emitted afterward. Imagine two lovers, one called X on galaxy P and the other Y on galaxy Q, and suppose that Q is about to cross P's horizon. Y tearfully radios goodbye to X, who, if the message is correctly timed, hears Y's goodbye infinitely distended:

goooddddbbbbbyyyyyeeee . . .

Thus X will hear Y's last message to the end of time, but nothing Y says subsequently can reach him. The phonograph record runs down but takes an infinite time to do so. An exactly similar situation applies to X's goodbye heard by Y. As the expansion proceeds with ever-increasing speed, more and more of P's neighboring galaxies will cross his horizon. Finally, P is alone in the visible world, but he can still see the galaxies as they were when they crossed the horizon. These ghostly galaxies show up by a very dim and very red light (because of the enormous Doppler effect at these great distances).

If the real universe is in fact a Lemaître universe, it makes sense to use that platitude, dear to politicians, "We are indeed living in historic times." The Lemaître model spends all but a minute fraction of its history in the eerie condition just described, in which every galaxy is living with the ghosts of its former neighbors. The fact that we can clearly see other galaxies in our neighborhood means that we are living in just this tiny fraction.

Lemaître has studied many details of his model which he profoundly believes to be a correct representation of the real universe. In particular, he has pictured the initial singular state as being the explosion of the "primeval atom" described in the previous chapter.

OTHER MODELS WITH COSMIC REPULSION

The models described in this chapter by no means exhaust the possibilities which arise if λ is included in the field equations. Another permissible model is shown in Figure 29. In this universe space is finite, and there is an infinite period of contraction, followed by a similar period of expansion.

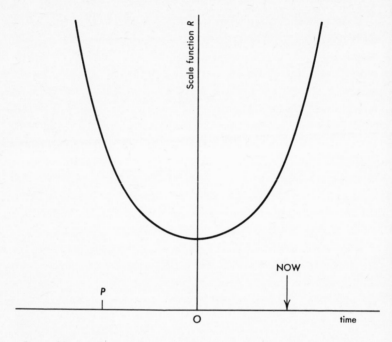

Figure 29. A MODEL WITH AN INFINITE PERIOD OF CONTRACTION. The separation between two typical galaxies, indicated by the scale function R, diminishes to a minimum value, and then begins to increase.

According to this model it should be possible at the present time to see back through the minimum value of R to times such as P when the galaxies had about the same separation as now, but were approaching one another: there should be a *violet* shift instead of a red shift if we look at very distant galaxies. This violet shift has not been observed, but it is likely that, if it exists, the telescopes have not yet penetrated far enough to observe it.

This model has an infinite past and future, and no singular state. It thus overcomes the difficulties described in Chapter 8. There are a number of questions that can be asked about it. For example, would all the stars have burned out during the model's infinite past? If so, this is a clear contradiction with observation. On the other hand, stars might have formed fairly recently, say at P: in this case, they would still have enough unburned hydrogen to be shining at the present time. This and other problems of the model have not yet been studied.

At the beginning of this chapter I expressed the hope that we shall not have to use Einstein's equations modified by the λ-term. For the reasons given there I think we should first try to find suitable models, like the simple ones of Chapter 7, which use the equations in their original form. If this proves impossible, there is a great variety of models like those of this chapter which can then be investigated.

does the universe rotate?

ROTATION

Kurt Gödel is a mathematician whose outstanding work is a theorem in logic. This theorem probably gets nearer than any other to the real foundations of mathematics, and incidentally shows that pure mathematicians have fewer grounds for being complacent about the self-consistency of their subject than they sometimes make out.

As a mathematicial logician, Gödel is world famous, but few people knew that he had an interest in physics as well. It was therefore a surprise when in 1949 he published an epoch-making paper on cosmology. In this paper he put forward a cosmological model in which the matter of the uni-

verse is *rotating.* This broke completely new ground: no one
had ever seriously suggested this before, and certainly nobody
had had the ingenuity to find a rotating solution of Einstein's
equations.

Before I describe Gödel's model, I must say something
about rotation. In Chapter 7 I explained the relative character of motion of one body with respect to another. This has
been generally understood for a long time, but the rotation
of a single body seems a different matter; there does not seem
to be anything relative about that. This indeed was the
opinion of Newton, who propounded, as an argument for the
existence of absolute motion, his famous *bucket experiment.*
An empty bucket is hung up by a twisted cord, held still,
then filled with water. At this stage water and bucket are at
rest (stage [i], Figure 30). The string is then allowed to
untwist. At first the surface of the water stays flat (stage [ii]),
but later, when the motion has been communicated to it, it
becomes curved and eventually rotates with the same speed as

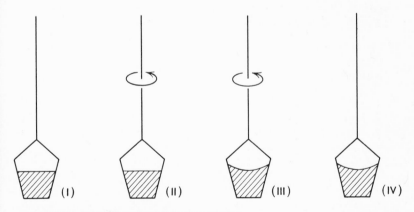

Figure 30. NEWTON'S BUCKET EXPERIMENT.
Stage (i). The bucket and the water are at rest.
Stage (ii). The bucket rotates.
Stage (iii). The bucket continues to rotate, and the water is also now rotating.
Stage (iv). The bucket is at rest, and the water is still rotating.

the bucket (stage [iii]), so that the two are at relative rest. Finally, the bucket is stopped and held fast, while the water continues for the time being to rotate (stage [iv]). In this last stage, the surface of the water is still curved.

Newton's analysis of the bucket experiment was in essence the following. In both stage (ii) and stage (iv) there was the same *relative* motion between the water and the bucket: for in (ii) the bucket rotates and the water is at rest, and in (iv) the bucket is at rest and the water rotates. Now, if rotation is a purely relative matter (like motion in a straight line with constant speed), then there should be no real difference in stages (ii) and (iv). *But in stage (ii) the surface was flat, whereas in stage (iv) it was curved. Hence there is a real difference,* and in (iv) the water is *really rotating,* whereas in stage (ii) the bucket is *really rotating.* From this Newton argued that rotation is absolute.

The bucket experiment has been the subject of argument for three hundred years, and I should not like to say that the controversy is over. The most determined opponents of Newton were Bishop George Berkeley, the great eighteenth century Irish philosopher, and Ernst Mach, nineteenth century Austrian physicist and philosopher. Berkeley's view was that rotation, like all other motion, is relative, but that rotation *relative to the fixed stars* produced mechanical effects such as the curvature of the water surface in the bucket. If, said Berkeley, all matter in the universe were annihilated except the bucket and its contents, it would be nonsense to speak of either of them as rotating absolutely.

Mach extended Berkeley's views a little. He pointed out that *geometrically* it makes no difference whether we say that the Earth rotates and the heavens are at rest, or that the Earth is at rest and the heavens rotate. According to Newton's mechanics we must choose the former interpretation, but this, said Mach, was a defect of Newton's theories. A proper theory of mechanics would not distinguish between the two hypotheses.

Einstein was deeply influenced by Mach's ideas, and tried to incorporate them in general relativity. Physicists are still arguing how far he was successful—and, if he was not, whether it really matters! It is certainly clear that Einstein's theory denies the validity of absolute rotation, but it is less clear whether it gives the fixed stars (now interpreted as distant galaxies because what were previously thought of as the fixed stars are now known to be moving about the center of the Milky Way) the prominence they should have according to Berkeley and Mach.

There is one important experimental fact bearing on this subject. I shall idealize it in the following way. Suppose a bucket experiment is done with great accuracy at the North Pole. Then it will be found that even when the bucket is not spinning relative to the Earth, the water surface is very slightly curved. Now let the bucket be rotated in such a way that, when the motion has been communicated to the water, the surface is completely flat. *It will be found that the bucket is at rest relative to the fixed stars.*

The interpretation of the experiment is this: At first the bucket and water rotated with the Earth, and this produced a slight curvature. When the water was given a rotation equal and opposite to that of the Earth, the surface was flat. This is exactly what Berkeley had said: that rotation *relative to the fixed stars* produces the curvature, and if there is no rotation relative to the fixed stars, the surface is flat. Those who do not accept Berkeley's views have to regard the result of the experiment simply as a coincidence.

Even today we do not understand rotation properly, and the strange properties of Gödel's rotating cosmological model underline this. Before describing Gödel's work, I must give some account of time in cosmology.

TIME IN COSMOLOGY

One of the ways in which relativity most outrages common sense is the havoc it plays with our ordinary ideas of time. The reader may have heard of what is called the twin paradox. One of the twins, say A, remains on Earth while the other one, B, sets out in a high-speed rocket and makes a journey through space. He eventually returns to the Earth having been away for, say, five years as judged by his clock, and by his bodily growth (for instance, the length of his beard). He finds that his twin brother A has aged perhaps ten years in his absence, as judged by A's clock and growth.

This paradox has been the subject of controversy ever since relativity was discovered. It is a result of special relativity, and does not rely on the high-powered mathematics of general relativity for its demonstration. The basic reason for it is that time is not absolute in relativity: for example, as mentioned in connection with de Sitter's model, two events which are simultaneous for A will not necessarily be simultaneous for B.

Once one has understood the fundamental ideas of relativity the twin experiment ceases to be a paradox, and indeed one would be surprised if the twins did not age differently. I have described how relativity introduces us to the idea of the space-time continuum, with four dimensions, three of space and one of time. Geometers call this continuum a four-dimensional space because it has many properties similar to those of ordinary three-dimensional spaces. The "points" of the four-dimensional space are events. An event is what we ordinarily understand by the word—a happening at a particular place at a particular time, like the departure of a spaceship. An event needs four numbers to specify it, namely, three space coordinates for the place, and one coordinate for the time.

We all know that there is more than one distance between two places: some routes are shorter than others. In the language of geometry this can be paraphrased: the interval between two points in three-dimensional space is not unique. In exactly the same way, the interval between two "points" (that is, events) in the four-dimensional space-time continuum is not unique. Intervals in three dimensions are measured by rulers, but in four dimensions different methods have to be used. One is to record the time on a clock which travels between the two events which lie at the ends of the interval.

Let us reconsider the twin experiment in the light of these ideas. The two events are the departure of B and his subsequent return, which I will denote by D and R. The fact that the twins are not together means that they take different routes in space-time between D and R; so the intervals between D and R are not the same for both. Since their clocks record the intervals for them, this implies that their clocks will show different times at the ends of B's journey.

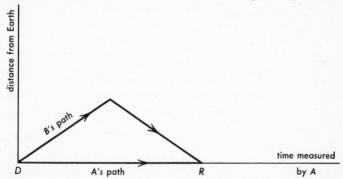

Figure 31. THE TWIN EXPERIMENT. The upward and downward sloping lines represent *B*'s outward and return journeys respectively.

We can represent this on a diagram, shown in Figure 31, in which the axes are the time measured by A, and distance from the Earth. Since A stays on the Earth, his space-time path is along the time axis; B's path is not. The lengths in the diagram of the two paths are not the same, corresponding to the fact that the intervals in space-time are different. The diagram is not a very effective way of representing paths in space-time, though it is about the best we can do on a sheet of paper. One misleading feature is that in the diagram B's path is longer than A's, whereas in four dimensions B's path is shorter.

What puzzles people about the twin experiment is that, according to relativity, it should be permissible for B to regard himself as at rest and to say that A goes on a journey. So it is. But then, argues the antirelativist, A should stay younger than B, which is a contradiction. The fallacy here is that though either twin may maintain that he is at rest and the other moves, *their experiences during the experiment are not equivalent.* A, who remains on the Earth, experiences no forces (except the negligible force of the Earth's gravity), but B's journey cannot be performed without rockets and retrorockets (or equivalent forces). Although it is not strictly true to say that the forces exerted by these rockets cause the time difference, they are indispensable to the motion that does cause it. And owing to these forces the experiences of A and B differ in an objective way, so they are not equivalent.

Because headaches like this are commonplace in relativity, it is a great good fortune that the relativistic world models which I have described in the previous chapters are free of them. This is because in these models there is a single cosmic time, the same for all galactic observers. I am careful to say *galactic* observers, meaning those at rest relative to the average motion of matter in their galaxy, because problems with time arise in cosmology if the observer is moving very fast with respect to his own galaxy. Fortunately, the Earth's motion is not far off the average for our Galaxy, so we count as galactic observers.

It is because of the existence of cosmic time that we can speak of the "age of the universe"; otherwise the age would vary with different observers and would not have much significance.

The comparatively straightforward temporal behavior of the ordinary cosmological models does not occur in Gödel's model, as we shall now see.

GÖDEL'S MODEL

I must make it clear that Gödel's model certainly does not represent our universe; this we know because in the model there is no expansion. The interest in it arises because some of its features may perhaps exist in our universe, and this would introduce some very strange phenomena.

In Gödel's model the universe does not expand, but it rotates. Because of the relative character of rotation we have to be more precise, and say what is meant by this statement. Suppose we lived in a Gödel universe, and imagine a terrestrial observer doing a bucket experiment. He hangs up his bucket and rotates it in such a way that, when the motion has been communicated to the water, the surface is completely flat. He then notices that relative to the water the heavens are rotating. On the other hand, if he arranges for the water to remain at rest with respect to the distant galaxies, he finds that the surface is curved.

Thus in Gödel's model the principle of Berkeley and Mach—that the water surface is flat when the bucket is at rest relative to the distant galaxies, and curved otherwise—is definitely untrue. Now because we know that the principle is true within the limit of observation, evidently the rotation of the universe, if any, must be very small. Nevertheless, if there were even a slight rotation it would have most interesting consequences, as we shall see.

At first, one is a little surprised to learn that Gödel's model satisfies the cosmological principle, that is to say, that all galactic observers in it would see the same picture of the universe. If we think of a rotating wheel, the axis of rotation seems to be in a special position. Similarly we might expect that there would be some definite axis about which the model rotates. However, this is not so: there is no special axis of rotation, but there is one through every point in space, and all these axes are parallel. Thus the cosmological principle is still satisfied, though there is the important difference from the ordinary cosmological models that in Gödel's model, although all points in space are equivalent, all directions of space are not, because the axis of rotation at every point defines a privileged direction.

In Gödel's model there is no universal time which all galactic observers can agree upon. Two such observers might, for example, attribute different ages to the same star; though if they knew enough about the theory of relativity they would be able to reconcile their discrepant results. Observers would also not agree on the *order* in which events occurred. Thus suppose two stars *A* and *B* were to explode; then one observer might say it was *A* that exploded first, while another might say it was *B*. This sort of temporal inversion is known to be possible from special relativity, so it is not very surprising to find it turning up in cosmology.

The most startling feature of Gödel's model is that *it is possible to travel back into the past*. Thus an observer at rest on his galaxy could board a rocket, perform a round trip (not necessarily at high speed), and *arrive before he started*. This recalls the limerick

> There was a young lady named Bright,
> Who could travel much faster than light.
> She departed one day,
> In the relative way,
> And returned on the previous night.

This was written many years ago, and has as basis a common misunderstanding that according to special relativity one can travel backward in time if one moves faster than the speed of light. Because special relativity does not permit any material object to move faster than light, the possibility does not arise. However, Gödel's model does allow one to travel into the past, and the speed of one's journey is largely irrelevant; what is important is the path one chooses to travel on.

The bewilderments of time travel have been well exploited by science-fiction writers. Perplexing situations can arise, such as that in which our great-great-great-grandchildren appear from the future to give us advice. Suppose that they tell us not to procreate children, and we obey! Is there a logical contradiction here? Such questions are posed by Gödel's model of the universe, but as yet scientists and philosophers have hardly considered them, let alone solved them.

MODELS WHICH ROTATE AND EXPAND

I said previously that Gödel's model cannot represent the actual universe because there is no expansion in it. However, there are models in which the universe expands as well as seeming to rotate about the observer. Now, there is at present no evidence in favor of a rotation, but there is no evidence against a very small rotation—and, of course, one never can be definitely ruled out: observations can only prescribe that the rotation be less than some limit. If there is a slight rotation, then the startling phenomena described in the previous section may occur in our actual universe. This is suggested particularly because the *speed* of rotation in Gödel's model does not seem to be especially important; it is only necessary that there shall be *some* rotation.

What temporal properties the expanding and rotating models have is not known, though pioneering work on them has been done by Professor O. Heckmann and his colleagues at Hamburg Observatory. This work has, however, revealed something of great interest about the start of the expansion of these models. In Chapter 8 I pointed out that what is needed to change a contraction of the universe into an expansion is a repulsive force between particles of matter. The rotating models provide just such a repulsion: namely, the centrifugal force due to the rotation. The scale function R for certain of them can show a minimum like that in Figure 29, in spite of the fact that no use is made of the λ-term. The models, therefore, offer the possibility of eliminating the unwanted singular state without introducing the λ-term.

summary of
relativistic theory

CLASSIFICATION

The reader may be excused for feeling some bewilderment at the variety of relativistic models described in Chapters 7, 9, and 10. To make the picture clearer, I shall now classify and summarize their important features.

(*a*) *Expanding models without cosmological term.* These, the Einstein–de Sitter, cycloidal, and hyperbolic models, were described in Chapter 7. They either go on expanding forever, or eventually contract. They all start from a singular state of infinite density, but I argued in Chapter 8 that this is a mathematical fiction.

These models are the simplest relativistic ones, and many cosmologists hope that the actual universe is one of these types.

(b) *Expanding models with cosmological term.* The checkered story of the cosmological term in Einstein's equations was described in Chapter 9, and it was explained how the presence of the term adds greatly to the variety of relativistic models. Of historical importance have been the static Einstein universe and Eddington's model. A particularly interesting model of this type is that due to Lemaître, which has a longer history than those of class (a).

Among these models are some without a singular state, for example, Eddington's model and the one whose scale function is shown in Figure 29.

(c) *Expanding and rotating models.* These models combine expansion with a general rotation of the matter in the universe, the possibility of which was first recognized in the researches of Gödel. Rotation introduces the strange temporal properties described in Chapter 10, and allows other interesting possibilities such as the removal of the singular state.

TOO MANY MODELS?

Some physicists think that a good cosmological theory should lead to a unique model of the universe, with one definite prediction about each observable relation such as Hubble's law. They argue that a good scientific theory should be capable of immediate disproof—that it should be highly vulnerable to observation. Relativistic cosmology, the argument runs, is not a good theory because it gives rise to a great many models, and cannot be disproved until all these have been shown to disagree with observation.

To assess the importance of this criticism, we must consider the nature of physical theories. Usually these give a number of simplified pictures, called models, of various physical phenomena, much as cosmology gives models of the universe. For instance, the theory of electricity gives a model of an electric charge, represented by a geometrical point, from which the electric field of the charge can be calculated. In a successful theory the models may either be correct, in which case they give a satisfactory representation of the phenomenon concerned, or they may be irrelevant. Thus in Newton's theory, if we ignore relativistic corrections, a point mass is a satisfactory model of the Sun. However, there is nothing in Newton's theory which forbids models of *negative* masses. A negative mass repels other masses instead of attracting them as an ordinary (positive) mass does. This model is neither right nor wrong, but irrelevant: there happens to be no physical realization of it. Nature just does not give us any examples of negative mass, at least as far as we know. The argument I am describing criticizes relativistic cosmology because it gives a number of irrelevant solutions of the cosmological problem.

It has not in the past been customary to criticize a theory for its irrelevant models. Indeed, sometimes these have been extremely valuable, since they have initiated a search for the phenomena they represent. The positron, an atomic particle, was predicted by the celebrated British physicist Paul Dirac in just this way. Now since, by definition, there is only one universe, this cannot happen in cosmology. Nevertheless, the irrelevant cosmological models are useful in stimulating ideas and researches which otherwise might not have come about. For example, there is no doubt that Gödel's model—which we *know* is irrelevant, since it does not expand—has made us think very hard again about the meaning of rotation, and of time.

On a mundane level, the multiplicity of models gives relativistic cosmological theory a flexibility which is very useful in practice. It saves us from getting ulcers every time astronomers make an incorrect cosmological observation, because the range of models is, usually, wide enough to accommodate the error. This is important too for a more serious reason. Suppose that relativistic cosmology were apparently falsified by some such mistake as occurred with the "age of the universe." This would mean that general relativity too would be under suspicion, and theorists would waste no end of time trying, unnecessarily, to find a new theory.

I must stress, though, that relativistic cosmology *could* be proved wrong, by which I mean that if certain things were observed, they could not be explained by relativistic theory. Indeed, if the steady-state theory is right, then relativistic cosmology is wrong, and, in my opinion, we have to scrap general relativity as well. I make this point because every scientific theory must be capable of *disproof;* otherwise it says nothing.

For these reasons, I am not greatly impressed by criticisms of the number of models we have in relativistic cosmology. It is instructive to note, however, from whom these criticisms come, namely from E. A. Milne and from the steady-state theorists. Now both Milne's theory and the steady-state theory were designed especially to solve the cosmological problem, so it is not remarkable that they both yield unique models. Moreover, both suffer from a common failing, that they lack a proper background of physical theory, as we shall see in the next chapter. Hence if there *is* any special credit in a theory which leads to a unique cosmological model—and of this I am very doubtful—it cannot be claimed either for Milne's theory or the steady-state theory.

I 2

the steady-state theory

ORIGIN

The learned physical journals since 1915 are littered with attempts to improve on, or simplify, or generalize, or just to play about with general relativity.

One of the reasons is the following. Probably the greatest part of Einstein's achievement was to discover the importance to physics of the geometry of four dimensions. Now, it is one thing to realize that physics and geometry are intimately connected, and quite another to decide in detail how the connection is to be implemented. The varieties of geometry are limited only by the imagination of pure mathematicians,

159

and the latter have invented a considerable number of geo-metries in the last hundred years. All of these are candidates for use in physics to describe four-dimensional space-time.

Quite naturally, many physicists have tried their luck at picking a geometry. After fifty years of effort, no one has managed to improve on Einstein, and we are left with the conclusion that not only did he discover the connection be-tween geometry and physics but also chose the best method of building this connection into a theory. This is a measure of his genius.

Of course, all these efforts have not been just for fun. There have been good reasons why many people, including Einstein himself, have thought that relativity is not the last word on the geometrization of physics. All who believe in the unity of science think it must be possible to unify the three great branches of physics—gravitation, electromagnet-ism, and the theory of the atom. This is why physicists have tried to generalize general relativity into what is called a *unified field theory*. A great number of such attempts were made, and all are on the scrapheap. This problem is still unsolved, and at present we hardly know how to begin.

Two important attempts have been made to alter rela-tivity for cosmological reasons, one by Milne and the other by Bondi, Gold, and Hoyle. The more radical is that of Milne who, while accepting special relativity, rejected gen-eral relativity altogether. Milne, like Eddington, aimed to explain physics by pure thought, almost without entering a laboratory or observatory. His program was extremely inter-esting. He began by asking, in effect, "Given people like us, who use light to observe events, who have an awareness of the passage of time, and so on, can we say from *this only* what the universe looks like?" In other words, Milne tried to build up physical theories assuming only a knowledge of our methods of perceiving and measuring.

The cosmological part of Milne's theory is remarkably successful. It leads to the very simple model of the universe described in Chapter 6, and according to Milne this is not, as it was for us, an oversimplification, but a rigorous and accurate result. The latest observations, described in Chapter 13, are not in agreement with this model, but they are not reliable enough for it to be finally ruled out.

To follow Milne's method is, as he put it, to submit one-self to a process of self-denial. None of the ordinary physical theories may be assumed, and everything must be deduced from his primitive postulates. To do this is a tremendous task, and that it was incomplete at the time of Milne's death is not surprising. However, every cosmological model should be based on an adequate theory of gravitation, since gravitational forces are important in the large-scale motions of matter, such as occur in the expansion of the universe. Relativistic cosmology fulfills this requirement because general relativity is a satisfactory gravitation theory, as we know for a number of reasons: for example, it correctly predicts the orbits of the planets. Now, Newton's theory does this too, except for certain minute discrepancies first observed in the case of the planet Mercury. Mercury's orbit is not a fixed ellipse as it should be according to Newton, but an ellipse whose major axis rotates. The rotation is very slow—it takes three million years for the axis to make one complete revolution—but astronomers were aware of it during the nineteenth century. General relativity accounts for the rotation with perfect accuracy, which is an important confirmation of the theory. Another striking validation—the bending of light—was referred to in Chapter 9. Milne was not able to deduce a satisfactory gravitation theory as a backing for his cosmology, and the one he put forward does not account for the observed facts of the solar system, for example, for the orbit of Mercury.

The approach through general relativity to cosmology is, of course, entirely different. Einstein's equations are assumed at the start, and the cosmological problem amounts to finding a special solution of them. But the equations are already well substantiated by their predictions about the Sun's gravitational field, so relativity provides not only a cosmology but also a satisfactory gravitation theory. Indeed, if we exclude atomic theory, relativity is in harmony with physics as a whole.

It is probably for this reason that Milne's theory is no longer a serious rival to relativistic cosmology. Very little work has been done on it since Milne's death in 1950, and at the present time interest is concentrated on relativistic cosmology and the steady-state theory.

The steady-state theory is an adaptation of relativity of an altogether different sort. It adopts the same geometrical approach, and has in many respects the same outlook as relativistic cosmology but differs on vital points of detail.

As has already been mentioned, the steady-state theory would probably not have been put forward had it not been for certain errors in the observations. In 1948 there seemed to be a conflict between the big bang models of general relativity (those of Chapter 7) and the "age of the universe." To be more precise, it appeared that the time T which had elapsed since the singular state of the models was less than the age of our own Galaxy, and this looked like a straightforward conflict between relativistic cosmology and observation. Even Einstein, never one to overrate the importance of observation, was worried by the discrepancy. There was actually a way in which the difficulty could have been overcome without endangering relativistic cosmology; namely, to admit the λ-term to the field equations and so obtain models, such as Lemaître's, with a longer time scale. However, Einstein's later prejudice against the λ-term has already been explained, and, rightly or wrongly, other cosmologists also felt that relativistic theory must rely on the three simple models of Chapter 7.

There is no doubt that the writings of the time showed a curious air of unbalance. For example, one investigation, by a pupil of no less a cosmologist than the famous American R. C. Tolman, considered the possibility of giving up the cosmological principle and adopting a model of the universe in which our Galaxy occupied a privileged position, somewhat like that of the Earth before Copernicus.

It was in this intellectual climate that in 1948 Bondi, Gold, and Hoyle put forward the steady-state theory. The great advantage of this theory was that it overcame the time-scale difficulty without giving up the cosmological principle. It had also the advantage of simplicity, and several serious disadvantages which many people were inclined to forgive at the time.

The three inventors of the theory, all colorful personalities, excellent speakers, and forceful writers, applied themselves zestfully to the task of convincing the world of the rightness of the steady-state theory. Some of the world showed its expected streak of obstinacy, but nevertheless solid progress was being made when suddenly the bubble burst.

In a report before the International Astronomical Union in Rome in September, 1952, Baade announced that the galactic distances then being used were serious underestimates, which must be multiplied by at least two (now thought to be five or more), for reasons which were explained in Chapter 4. Baade's figures were accepted by all immediately, partly on account of his distinction as an astronomer, but also because no one could argue against the results of the world's largest telescope, of which Baade had almost exclusive use.

The effect of the new results on cosmological theory soon became clear. I can explain this with the help of our simplified model of Chapter 6. The time since the start of the expansion was there shown to be

$$T = \frac{\text{distance of a galaxy } G \text{ from us now.}}{\text{speed of } G}$$

Now, Baade's results made no difference to the speed of G, which was reliably determined by the red shift; but the distance in the numerator had to be doubled, and so T had to be doubled. *The age of the universe was twice as great as previously thought,* and the time-scale difficulty of relativistic cosmology disappeared between the start and finish of Baade's lecture.

Thus the steady-state theory became unnecessary in September, 1952. However, its originators showed a sturdy reluctance to recognize the fact. No longer able to claim it as the only theory in accordance with observation, Bondi, Gold, and Hoyle found other virtues in it, and continued their task of proselytization with considerable effect. Now, when the theory seems to stand on the verge of final disproof by observation, let us take a look at it and assess the part it has played in the development of cosmology.

THE PERFECT COSMOLOGICAL PRINCIPLE

Relativistic cosmology assumes the cosmological principle which, it will be remembered, states that all galactic observers at a given time see essentially the same picture of the universe. In the steady-state theory a stronger version of this is adopted, called the perfect cosmological principle. This states that all galactic observers see essentially the same picture of the universe at *all times.*

Now, one feature of the universe that must appear the same at all times is the average density of matter. However, it is known that the universe is expanding, and as we have seen in previous chapters, this leads to a thinning out of galaxies and therefore to a gradual diminution in the average density. The apparent contradiction is overcome in the steady-state theory by supposing that matter is continually created out of nothing in empty space and that this newly created matter keeps the density always at the same value, in spite of the expansion.

Steady-state theorists maintain that the perfect cosmological principle is the linchpin of the whole theory. Indeed, Bondi goes so far as to suggest that cosmology without it is at best an extremely hazardous business, and at worst a quite impossible undertaking. His reason for believing this is that if the universe has been, or will be, very different from what it is now, we have no warrant for supposing that our scientific laws will apply in those circumstances; in fact, we are not justified at all in trying to apply these laws to the remote past or future. Thus the perfect cosmological principle becomes, according to Bondi, almost a necessary condition for cosmology to be possible.

This view has many opponents, among them the redoubtable Herbert Dingle, formerly Professor of History and Philosophy of Science at London University, and now retired. Dingle insists that the perfect cosmological principle is an assumption no more compelling than others made in cosmology. As he said to the Royal Astronomical Society in London in 1953: "Let us call a spade a spade and not a perfect agricultural principle." Dingle's view is, of course, that the perfect cosmological principle can well be false, and if it is, then we shall have to do without it and use such laws as we have to extrapolate tentatively into the past and the future. As I pointed out in Chapter 7, this procedure is common enough in astrophysics, and there nobody makes a song and dance about it.

Nevertheless, we can agree with Bondi and his colleagues on one thing: the perfect cosmological principle is a statement of great power which leads to a clear and definite cosmological model.

THE STEADY–STATE MODEL

It is important to understand that the steady-state universe is not static. Change is going on all the time, but the overall picture does not alter. The galaxies recede from one another, and new ones, formed by condensation out of the newly created matter, take the places of the old ones which have moved away. There is a process of constant renewal and unceasing motion. As Bondi remarks, a good analogy is a river, which preserves a steady state, although its component droplets are continually in motion.

We can draw a graph of the scale function of the steady-state model, much as we did for the relativistic models. Consider an observer O and suppose he focuses attention on a particular galaxy, G, whose distance, R, he continually measures. Now let O draw the graph of R against time: the result will be as in Figure 32. As time passes, G recedes from O at an ever-increasing rate: the recession of any particular galaxy speeds up with time. The graph has a definite start because G comes into existence at some definite time, namely, the time at which it condenses out of the created material.

The steady-state model has a horizon rather like that in Lemaître's model (Chapter 9). The galaxy G will eventually reach O's horizon, and though it will continue to be dimly visible, no signal emitted later than a certain instant can ever reach O from it. As in Lemaître's model, the space between O and G is then expanding so rapidly that light cannot travel fast enough to cover the increasing separation between them.

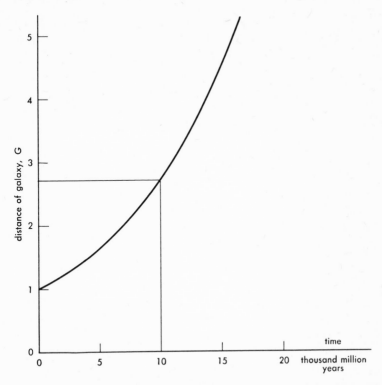

Figure 32. THE STEADY-STATE MODEL. The graph shows the distance of a galaxy which comes into existence at the moment indicated by zero in the figure. After 10,000 million years, the distance from the observer is nearly three times the initial distance.

CONTINUAL CREATION OF MATTER

The most controversial feature of the theory is the creation of matter. It is important to understand that this matter is created not out of radiation or something else, but *out of nothing*. The rate of creation is extremely small—one hydrogen atom is supposed to be created in a pint volume every ten years, which is equivalent to one-tenth of a gram each second in the entire volume of the solar system. It is clear

that such a slow rate will be very hard to detect directly and
also that no conflict with observation is involved on this point,
or is likely to be in the immediate future.

Although the creation rate is extremely small, the fact
that the model demands one at all amounts to a contraven-
tion of a very important physical law—the law of conservation
of energy. This is because, according to special relativity,
matter is a form of energy; thus if matter is created, so is
energy, and the conservation law is not fulfilled. It is important to be clear what this means, especially as the steady-state
theorists themselves have written rather tendentiously on this
subject. Bondi, for example, writes as follows: "In the steady-
state model the amount of matter is constant in the part of
the universe observable with a telescope of given power, that
is, in the part within any fixed distance from the observer.
. . . In the relativistic models, on the other hand, the
amount of matter in a similarly defined part of the universe
is diminishing. . . . It may well be considered more correct
to speak of the conservation of mass in the steady-state model
rather than in relativity. . . ."

Now, this point of view cannot be maintained without
grossly distorting what is meant by the conservation of mass
(which, in this context, is the same as the conservation of
energy). Let us consider the region V surveyed by the observer's telescope, and suppose that he counts the number
of galaxies in V at two instants t_1 (earlier) and t_2 (later).
What we ordinarily mean by the conservation of mass in V
is:

> No. of galaxies in V at time t_1
> $=$ No. in V at time t_2 $+$ no. which have receded over the
>   boundary between t_1 and t_2.

This form of conservation is automatically ensured in general relativity.

In the steady-state theory the "law of conservation" is:

$$\text{No. in } V \text{ at } t_1 = \text{No. in } V \text{ at } t_2,$$

irrespective of the number crossing the boundary between t_1 and t_2. To say that this implies conservation is, in my opinion, a misuse of language. If a magician conjures a rabbit out of thin air, the trick is not explained if the rabbit runs out of the room, even though the number of rabbits in the room is then the same as it was initially (in this case, none).

Indeed, steady-state theorists sometimes seem to admit that their theory does infringe the conservation law. For example, D. W. Sciama of Cambridge, England, referring to the continual creation of matter, writes: "This suggestion is, of course, inconsistent with the conservation of matter."

Now, there is nothing sacred about the law of conservation of energy. It is a law which has been found to be correct in the past, and now has a very wide application—in fact, it is used daily in every branch of physics and chemistry. Like every other scientific law, it will be given up immediately if a single infringement of it is established by experiment. But scientists will not give it up unless very definite evidence against it is forthcoming, and this the steady-state theory does not provide. I shall return to this question later in this chapter.

According to the theory, matter is created at a rate which is, on the average, constant over space and throughout time. When a particle appears, it begins to move with the average velocity of matter in its neighborhood. It is thought most likely that matter is created in the form of hydrogen atoms or neutrons.

That creation is supposed to occur evenly throughout space distinguishes the steady-state theory from another in which creation out of nothing is assumed, namely, that of the German physicist Pascual Jordan. Jordan proposes that the created matter appears in the form of exploding stars (supernovae). His theory is not developed primarily as a cosmology, and its cosmological consequences are less clear cut than those of the steady-state theory. Jordan's work has been subjected to severe criticism both by Bondi and by Heckmann, and it seems that further development will be needed before it has to be considered as a serious rival to the two main contemporary theories.

THE FORMATION OF GALAXIES

The steady-state model, because it is definite and simple, has had its details worked out to a greater extent than the relativistic models. One feature, which has been the subject of extensive investigations, is the process by which galaxies form in it. The problem is this. Matter is supposed to be created as single particles, and in some way these must aggregate into stars and galaxies. Further, the aggregation must stop when the galaxies reach their observed size—it must not go on indefinitely. In other words, there must be a maximum size for galaxies, and the theory must account for this, and also show that the entire system of galaxies is a self-perpetuating one; otherwise, this system would not be in a steady-state, which would be contrary to the hypothesis of the theory.

These problems have been studied in detail by Sciama. Although it cannot be said that he has answered every question that can be raised, it is clear that a good start has been made.

By contrast, the theory of formation of galaxies in the relativistic models is in a much less satisfactory state. The problem to be solved is different. Let us take the relativistic models that begin with a big bang; during the initial period of extremely high temperature, we must assume that matter is in a gaseous form, say, of hydrogen, and is very evenly distributed. Then we have to explain how the manifest heterogeneity of the universe, namely, the galaxies, has resulted from this extremely homogeneous start. The reader will notice the difference between this and the corresponding problem in the steady-state theory, according to which the universe never has been homogeneous.

The relativistic problem turns out to be very puzzling, and has not yet been solved. It is known that the initial homogeneous gas would be gravitationally unstable, and would tend to collapse into condensations, but only very slowly. Reckoning about 10,000 million years from the singular state, we find that there has not been enough time for the galaxies to form by this mechanism. Only in Lemaître's model, in which a time scale longer than 10,000 million years is permitted, can condensations form.

I do not think that anyone believes that we should rule out all relativistic models except Lemaître's on these grounds: the last word has certainly not yet been said on this question, but it is interesting that the steady-state theory, in my opinion defective in so many respects, should have the advantage on this issue.

THE SECOND LAW OF THERMODYNAMICS

In the early books on cosmology, particularly those written by Jeans and Eddington in the 1920's and 1930's, the second law of thermodynamics occupied a prominent place. This law has many forms, and I want to illustrate it by a definite example. Suppose that we have two boxes, one containing hydrogen (*A*), and the other evacuated (*B*) (Figure 33). Now imagine that a small connecting hole is opened: the second law of thermodynamics states that provided the two boxes are isolated from the rest of the universe, the gas

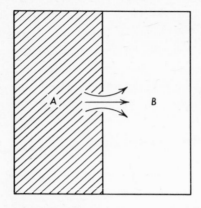

Figure 33. THE SECOND LAW OF THERMODYNAMICS. The chamber A is initially full of gas and B is empty. When the hole is opened, gas starts to diffuse into B.

will eventually be equally divided between the two compartments. The law goes further, and states that after the hole has been opened the gas will never again be in its initial state.

During the experiment a process of equalization has taken place: diversity has been replaced by uniformity. Theoretical physicists measure uniformity by a quantity called entropy, and, according to the second law, the entropy of an isolated system will increase, or, to be more precise, will never decrease. A characteristic of these equalization processes is that, although energy is conserved, it is no longer available in such a useful form at the end as it was at the beginning. Another example is that if two bodies at different temperatures are brought into contact and then isolated from the rest of the universe, their temperatures will eventually become equal.

This equalization is, according to the second law, going on all around us all the time. Eventually the whole universe will reach a state of uniform chemical composition and of temperature, and then nothing more will ever happen. This is the famous "heat death" of Jeans and Eddington. Of course, it is going to take a very long time for the complete equalization to take place; but since, as cosmologists, we are accustomed to thinking of long periods, the "heat death" is certainly part of our business.

The verdict of Jeans and Eddington then is that in the absence of some process for rejuvenation of the universe, it will die an ignoble death of creeping paralysis. Any relativistic model with an infinite past, such as a permanently oscillating one (Chapter 8), would be ruled out on these grounds. The steady-state model, though its past is infinite, is, however, in no danger because the creation process is one of disequalization, which provides the universe with a continual shot in the arm.

Now, the second law of thermodynamics is a very queer law—just how queer, Maxwell showed a hundred years ago when he invented his famous demon. Imagine our experiment with the two boxes concluded, so that the hydrogen is evenly distributed in both chambers. The gas consists, of course, of molecules flying about in all directions. Suppose now that a demon sits at the hole and can operate a shutter. He does this so that whenever there arrives at the hole a molecule going from *B* to *A* he lets it through, and whenever a molecule is going from *A* to *B* he drops the shutter and stops it. In due course *A* is full again and *B* empty, contradicting the second law.

To my knowledge no satisfactory explanation of the paradox has ever been given. In Maxwell's day it seemed very farfetched to suppose that it would ever be possible to sort out molecules by simple mechanical means, as the demon does. With modern methods it can no longer be regarded as completely impossible. In any case, whether the sorting process can be carried out in practice is merely a technical question which does not affect the principle behind Maxwell's objection.

What is clear is that the second law deals with *probabilities:* it is highly probable that initially the gas in box *A* will diffuse into B, but it is not certain. Eddington realized this when he said that one day we might put a kettle on a hot stove and find that the water froze. This is highly unlikely but not impossible.

To look at the subject in another way, we can say that the second law is a statement concerning the *information* we have about a system. This point was emphasized many years ago by the famous American chemist G. N. Lewis. If we had enough knowledge of the positions and velocities of the molecules of water when we put the kettle on the stove, we should be able to say quite definitely whether it would freeze or boil. In the absence of this information we appeal to the second law, which tells us the most probable result.

The second law therefore says that entropy increases except when it doesn't. It is not a law in the same sense as Newton's law of gravitation, which tells us the force between gravitating masses in *all* circumstances. The second law can be false if the initial conditions of the experiment are exceptional.

To me, therefore, the second law has not the compelling force in cosmology that it had for Eddington and Jeans. I think that it can, so to speak, be overruled by other laws of nature. If we wish to adopt a model in which the entropy does not increase, then though the second law may say this model is improbable, it cannot rule it out. Moreover, there may be some perfectly good reason why the entropy should not continually increase in some models—for example, in the permanently oscillating model (Chapter 8, Figure 24) there may be some process operating near the minima which decreases entropy, though we do not yet know what this may be.

There is another reason why the second law is not now taken so seriously in cosmology. It has never been shown to apply to the universe as a whole, especially to an infinite universe.

Thus although in this matter of the "heat death" the steady-state theory has an automatic answer in its continual creation, the relativistic models are not, in my opinion, threatened, at any rate at present. What is needed is some careful investigation of the applicability of the second law of thermodynamics to the universe as a whole, taking into account general relativity theory. Only when this has been successfully done can we judge whether the relativistic models need to be amended in the light of the second law.

FOR AND AGAINST THE STEADY–STATE THEORY

The steady-state theory has a number of attractive features. In the first place, the idea of a universe unchanging on a large scale is a simple one, and one which many people find aesthetically pleasing. Second, the problems of the singular state, which cause so much trouble in the relativistic models, are completely absent. Because the average density and temperature, like all other large-scale properties of the steady-state model, are unchanging, the question of a period when these were very high does not arise.

The absence of a singular state in the steady-state theory was at first thought to be a defect because a big bang was considered necessary to provide the conditions required for the formation of the heavy elements. However, as I explained in Chapter 8, the recent demonstration that these elements can form in stars has removed the need for a big bang, and this objection to the steady-state theory no longer exists.

One of the important defects of the theory, that it infringes the law of conservation of energy, has already been referred to. The infringement is by a very small amount, and the authors of the theory seem to suggest that it is therefore of slight importance. I am reminded of the old story about the girl who gave birth to an illegitimate baby, and excused herself on the grounds that it was, after all, only a very small baby. Contemporary physics is based on the law that in all changes whatever, energy is strictly conserved. By this is meant that however accurate the measurements, the law will be verified within the error of the experiment. The steady-state theory implies that when the accuracy reaches a certain level, the law will be found to be false. If true, this is of tremendous importance, and it must sweep away many of the most fundamental parts of physics.

Let us therefore be entirely clear on this. The change proposed by introducing continual creation is a revolutionary one, and before we turn physics upside down we must make quite sure that it is really necessary.

The other main objection to the steady-state theory is that it is not in the ordinary sense a fundamental theory at all. The most important part of it is missing. *No explanation is given of why the universe is expanding.* In the relativistic theory this explanation lies in Einstein's field equations, with or without the λ-term. *In the steady-state theory there are no field equations.* The steady-state model has been put forward, but with no mathematical background: it is a phenomenological model, based on the perfect cosmological principle but little else.

Phenomenological theories are useful either in applied science or in pure science when it is at a primitive level. For example, Boyle's law states that if the temperature of a given mass of gas is kept constant, the pressure is inversely proportional to the volume. Boyle proposed this law in 1662 purely on the basis of experiments: it was then a phenomenological law. Two centuries later, Boyle's law was explained in terms of the motions of the molecules which make up the gas. It then ceased to be phenomenological and became part of theoretical physics.

The position of the steady-state theory is somewhat similar to that of Boyle's law in its early stage—except that the former is not similarly well founded on observation. Several attempts have been made to equip the model with a theoretical backing. Hoyle, to his credit, has been looking for suitable field equations ever since 1948, and he has so far proposed three different sets. I think, however, that even he will be prepared to agree that his attempts have not yet been successful.

In 1960, Bondi and R. A. Lyttleton put forward the idea of an "electric universe," intended to account for the expansion in the steady-state model. A feature of the idea is that the electric charges of the proton and the electron are not *exactly* equal and opposite (as is usually supposed), but differ very slightly in magnitude. It does not particularly matter which is greater, but let us assume that it is the proton: then a hydrogen atom is not electrically neutral, but has a very slight positive charge. Hence two hydrogen atoms, since both will be positively charged, repel each other very weakly. If we now imagine a large mass of hydrogen atoms, there will be two opposing tendencies: on the one hand, gravitation will tend to hold the mass together, and on the other, the electrical repulsion will tend to make it disintegrate. A calculation shows that if the charge excess on the proton is large enough, the disintegrating tendency will predominate. The electrical repulsion can in this way cause an expansion of the universe.

The hypothesis that the proton has a charge excess was tested experimentally by A. M. Hillas and T. E. Crankshaw of Harwell, England, in 1959. They found that the excess of charge is less than that required by Bondi and Lyttleton, whose theory seems, therefore, to be in direct conflict with observation. In any case, the steady-state model as augmented by this electric theory contravenes not only the conservation of mass but also the conservation of charge—another well-attested law of physics, which states that electric charge is never created or destroyed. It is not surprising that the theory of the electric universe has not met with a very enthusiastic response.

The steady-state model is therefore still without a theoretical basis, and at present can be regarded as hardly more than speculation.

the decision

13

the most recent
observations

OBJECTIVE

We theoretical cosmologists can argue indefinitely about
the logic and aesthetics of our theories, but observers always
have the last word. In this chapter I want to give an up-to-
date account of the most important observational tests of
cosmology. I hope I can communicate to the reader some of
the excitement we feel now that we are at last on the thres-
hold of decision between some of our many cosmological
models.

THE LATEST ABOUT HUBBLE'S LAW

I explained in Chapter 5 that Hubble's law, namely,

$$\text{red shift} = \text{constant} \times \text{distance} \qquad (4)$$

is certainly true for nearby galaxies, but may need correction for distant ones. This was the opinion of M. Humason, N. Mayall, and A. Sandage in 1956 when they published their results on eighteen clusters of galaxies. However, later and more accurate observations by W. A. Baum of Palomar suggest that the law is accurately true out to distances of more than 4,000 million light-years. We can calculate from theory the form that the law would take for the various models described in previous chapters, and some results are shown in the graph in Figure 34. The crosses indicate the observed points, and Baum draws a straight line through them, as shown.* The Figure also contains the theoretical curves for two models. It will be seen that neither the Einstein–de Sitter nor the steady-state model is a satisfactory representation of the data. A good fit with Baum's straight line can be obtained with the cycloidal model of Chapter 7, whose expansion curve is shown in Figure 18.

It would be wrong, though, to suggest that these results are in any way final. It is obvious that there is a good deal of scatter in the observed points, and this indicates that the results are by no means certain, in spite of Baum's painstaking work. A number of possible causes of inaccuracy has been suggested.

---

* Results of experiments and observations inevitably contain errors, and it is necessary to find the graph which fits them best. In Baum's work the best fit is a straight line like the one shown. The task of the theorist is then to produce a theoretical curve which coincides with that found by the observer.

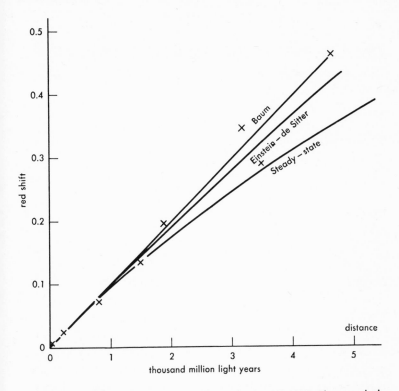

Figure 34. THE LATEST OBSERVATIONS ON HUBBLE'S LAW. The actual observations are represented by crosses. Baum's straight line through the observed points is as shown, and the theoretical curves for the Einstein–de Sitter, and for the steady-state models lie beneath this. The cycloidal model gives a good approximation to Baum's straight line.

First, there is the usual difficulty in estimating distances of far-away galaxies, referred to in Chapter 4. It is necessary to know accurately the distance of one galaxy in order to calibrate the distance-scale obtained from the measurements of apparent brightness, and we cannot yet be sure that we do know this correctly. If a mistake occurred here it would affect the slope of Baum's line, but it would remain straight. Such an error, then, would not help to reconcile Baum's results with either the Einstein–de Sitter or the steady-state models.

Another uncertainty surrounds what are called "evolutionary effects." The light from the most distant of Baum's galaxies left its source over 4,000 million years ago. The stars at that time may have been appreciably brighter or dimmer than they are now. Baum's points have been worked out ignoring this possibility and assuming that the energy output has not changed in the intervening period. If the stars were brighter at the time of emission, this means that the galaxies are really more distant than Baum has calculated, and his line should be a curve. Thus evolutionary effects might reconcile Baum's observations with the Einstein–de Sitter model.

The possibility of evolution is ruled out in the steady-state model because, by the perfect cosmological principle, the universe is supposed to stay the same on a large scale. Nevertheless, it is possible to alter the theory, as Hoyle has recently done, so that some evolutionary effects may be expected. These arise, according to Hoyle, because the phrase "on a large scale" is open to different interpretations. The matter becomes even more important to the steady-state theorists in their analysis of the results of the radio observations, and their views will be described more fully when Ryle's results are discussed later in this chapter.

As if the two foregoing uncertainties in Baum's work were not enough, the statisticians have pointed out a further possible source of error. When statistical methods are used, it is important to choose a random sample, and it may be questioned whether Baum's very small sample of the myriads of clusters of galaxies is really random. It has been suggested that the unfortunate observer, in trying to find clusters which show a large red shift—and the larger the red shift, the better the chance of proving or disproving Hubble's law—unconsciously chooses clusters that contain giant galaxies which are unusually bright. In this way a bias would be introduced into the sample, and the results would not represent the universe as a whole.

This is a particularly difficult objection to answer. Indeed, it is rather hard to see how one could really dispose of it. We can only hope that, as techniques improve, larger samples of galaxies can be studied and the possibility of selecting a biased sample can be reduced.

Baum's is the most recent of a series of observations at Palomar on Hubble's law. Previous observations in the series were those of Abell, and of Humason, Mayall, and Sandage referred to earlier. The results of these three surveys do not agree as closely as one would like, even when, as happened (intentionally) in a few cases, the observers were examining the same cluster. Nevertheless, there is agreement at least on one thing: that a serious discrepancy exists between observation and the steady-state theory in its simple form (that is, as it was before Hoyle modified it).

THE CONCLUSIONS FROM RADIO ASTRONOMY

In Chapter 5 I referred to number counts of galaxies. These have been carried out by optical and also by radio observations. In both cases what is done in effect is to count the number, N, of galaxies inside a sphere of radius, r, light-years, then to change r and count again, and so on. In this way, N is obtained as a function of r. Information of this sort was published by Hubble as long ago as 1936, but there are many difficulties in getting accurate results. In later years optical astronomers have relied more on the red shift-distance measurements.

Extremely important work on number counts has recently been done in radio astronomy. The method is, in principle, the same as that described above, the distance being measured by the faintness of the radio source. What the radio astronomers do in practice is to count the number of radio sources, N, whose power is greater than a certain amount, S. By power is meant the power measured at the radio receiver, and the technical name for this is "flux density"; it is measured in units called watts per square meter per cycle per second bandwidth. When the N has been counted for one particular S, another S is chosen, and the count repeated. In this way a table can be constructed showing the dependence of N on S, and the data plotted on a graph.

Suppose for the moment that the universe consists of galaxies, all equally powerful, at rest, and evenly distributed throughout space. Then the graph, plotted on a logarithmic scale, should be a straight line with downward slope $1\frac{1}{2}$.* What is meant by the slope of a line is illustrated in Figure 35. Lines such as PQ and PR are drawn parallel to the axes as shown, and the ratio $\dfrac{PQ}{PR}$ is called the slope.

The latest graph obtained by M. Ryle and his colleagues at Cambridge is shown in Figure 36, in which the broken line is inclined at a slope of $1\frac{1}{2}$ for comparison. It will be seen that Ryle's graph is a straight line, but that it is steeper than the broken line, so that its slope is greater than $1\frac{1}{2}$; in fact the

---

* Consider the number of galaxies, N, inside a sphere centered on the Milky Way, with radius r: then, since the volume of the sphere is $\frac{4}{3}\pi r^3$, N varies as r^3. The flux density, S, of a galaxy, G, on the surface of the sphere, like the apparent brightness, varies as $\dfrac{1}{r^2}$. Let us now suppose that all galaxies inside the sphere appear brighter than G (because they are nearer), and all those outside appear fainter. Eliminating r, we have

$$N \text{ varies as } \frac{1}{S^{3/2}};$$

or

$$\log N \text{ varies as } -\frac{3}{2}\log S,$$

so that the slope of the graph of $\log N$ against $\log S$ is $-\dfrac{3}{2}$, or $1\frac{1}{2}$ downward.

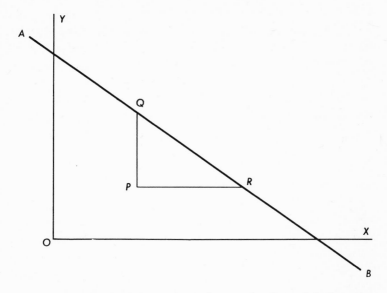

Figure 35. THE SLOPE OF A STRAIGHT LINE. The slope of the line AB is obtained by drawing the straight lines RP, QP parallel to the coordinate axes OX and OY. The slope is the ratio PQ/PR.

slope is 1.8. On the same figure is shown the shape which the graph should have if either the steady-state or the Einstein–de Sitter model were correct.

Several points arise concerning Figure 36. First, we need feel no surprise that the results do not lie on the broken line because this refers to a static universe, which we know is incorrect. Second, we ask what we can infer from the discrepancy between the actual and the dotted lines. Now, as the actual line is steeper, it means that at *low* flux densities (left of figure) the number of galaxies is *greater* than in the static case. Now, a low flux density means that the galaxy is faint, and therefore distant. Hence the radio sources are more numerous at great distance: *there is an excess of distant sources.* Schematically we can picture the situation as in

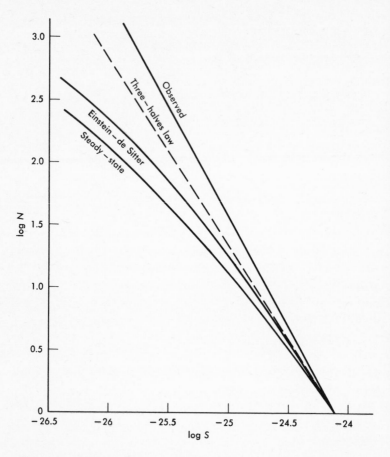

Figure 36. THE LATEST RADIO OBSERVATIONS. Ryle's straight line through the observed points lies above the theoretical lines corresponding to the three-halves law, the Einstein–de Sitter model, and the steady-state model.

Figure 37, which illustrates the relative dearth of galaxies near the observer O.

Why are radio sources more plentiful at great distance? The reason is one that has been mentioned before: as we look out into space we look back into time. The light now reaching us from the radio galaxy 3C 295 left its source 4,000 mil-

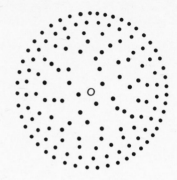

Figure 37. THE EXCESS OF DISTANT SOURCES. The dots represent sources, and these are more densely distributed at greater distances.

lion years ago, and we see it as it then was. Therefore, if the universe was different in the past from what it is now, we can find this out by examining very distant parts.

According to the steady-state theory, which says that the universe has always been much the same as it is now, this inspection of the past should reveal nothing different from the present. In particular, the density of radio sources should be the same on the average as it is now.

Actually, the position is not quite so simple. The reader will notice that the curve in Figure 36 representing the steady-state model is different from the straight line of slope $1\frac{1}{2}$ which represents the static universe. Why, it may be asked, if we see the same thing when we look back into the past, should the steady-state curve not be the same as that for the static case?

The answer is that the steady-state model is stationary but not static. Although things stay the same on the average, it is not true that nothing is moving. The galaxies recede, and the light and radio waves from them are red shifted. It is this red shift which causes the discrepancy in the two curves, as will now be explained.

It will be recalled from Chapter 5 that a red shift weakens the light received; also, the greater the distance of a galaxy, the greater the red shift and the larger the weakening effect.

Imagine now two equal, large spherical regions, one in a static universe which obeys the $1\frac{1}{2}$-power law, and the other in the steady-state model. Let us suppose that the two regions contain equal numbers of radio galaxies, all with the same output. The energy received at the center O from a galaxy A on the surface (see Figure 38) will be different in the two cases because in the steady-state model (case [ii]) the radiation is weakened by the red shift. Consider the energy received at O from A in the static case (i), and let it be, say, 10^{-26} watts per square meter per cycle per second. Then according to our assumption that all radio galaxies inside the sphere have the same power, all N of them will give rise to a flux density equal to this or greater.

In the steady-state model (ii), however, A will not give such a large flux density, because of the red shift. The source B which just does give a flux density of 10^{-26} will be nearer O, and the sources with flux density greater than or equal to 10^{-26} will lie on or inside the dotted sphere. Their number will be less than N. Hence in the steady-state model the curve

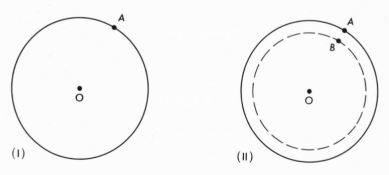

Figure 38. THE DEPENDENCE OF NUMBER COUNTS ON THE RED SHIFT. The diagrams (i) and (ii) refer to equal regions, each containing equal numbers of galaxies, in a static universe and in the steady-state model respectively. In the former there is no red shift; in the latter the red shift weakens the radio waves. For this reason the galaxy B in (ii) would give the same flux density as A in (i).

in Figure 36 lies beneath the straight line with slope $1\frac{1}{2}$ which represents the static model.

The red shift has a similar effect on the Einstein–de Sitter graph. In this model, the galaxies, and therefore presumably the radio sources, were closer together in the past than they are now, and so as we look out into distant space we should see a denser distribution. This means that, if it were not for the red shift, the curve for the Einstein–de Sitter model would be *above* the dotted line: however, the weakening effect of the red shift brings it below this line, though not so far below as that for the steady-state model.

The reader may wonder why we do not make some correction for the red shift, and thereby present the graphs in a clearer form. The reason is that we cannot "correct" the observed data without assuming some definite model of the universe, and then the "correction" depends on the model adopted. This matter is tied up with the ambiguities in the definition of distance, referred to in Chapter 4. If distance could be unambiguously defined, then we could represent N as a function of the distance instead of the flux density. However, the distance of the galaxy (or radio source) with a certain apparent brightness (or flux density) depends on the model chosen to represent the universe. Hence we are no better off using distance, and we might as well keep to the variable we observe directly, namely, the flux density.

Let us therefore take Figure 36 as it stands to represent Ryle's results and their comparison with

(a) the steady-state model,
(b) the Einstein–de Sitter model.

Accepting the observed data as correct (see, however, the next section), we can draw the following conclusions.

First, *the steady-state model diverges very markedly from Ryle's straight line, and seems to be incompatible with these observations.* Two courses seem to be open to those who wish to save the theory. They can either dispute the correctness of Ryle's work or alter the theory. These alternatives will be considered in the next two sections.

Second, the Einstein–de Sitter model also seems to be at variance with observation. However, as has been shown by W. Davidson of London, there are possible explanations for this, not available to the steady-state theory, at least in its original simple form. Let us suppose, for example, that radio sources become weaker as they grow older. Then the sources we see at great distance are stronger than those near to us, because they are younger. Now the curve for the Einstein–de Sitter model in Figure 36 was calculated on the assumption that the sources do not change with time. If we recalculate it on the basis of our new hypothesis, this has the effect of raising the top left-hand portion, and, by supposing a suitable rate of weakening with age, it can be brought into agreement with Ryle's line.

Thus we can still believe in the Einstein–de Sitter model if we assume this type of evolution in radio sources. We know so little about these sources that we cannot say whether this evolution does occur or not. It is certainly possible that the sources have changed appreciably over the billions of years since the start of the expansion. So we can say at least that the evolutionary hypothesis, which saves the Einstein–de Sitter model, cannot be ruled out.

This hypothesis could not be used to save the steady-state theory. By the perfect cosmological principle, radio sources, like everything else, must on the average stay always the same, and no systematic evolution is possible. The steady-state theory cannot be reconciled with Ryle's straight line by this argument, although as mentioned in connection with Baum's optical work, Hoyle has tried to alter the model to permit some evolution to occur.

The evolutionary hypothesis is available to any model but the steady-state one. The simple relativistic models give a log N — log S curve rather like that of the Einstein–de Sitter model, and to bring them into agreement with Ryle's results some evolution has to be assumed. As just explained, there is at present nothing against such evolution, so the relativistic models (or, at least, some of them) can be reconciled with the observations by these means.

IS RYLE RIGHT THIS TIME?

In Chapter 5 I wrote of the difficulties of radio astronomy, and referred to the mistakes of the past. We must ask ourselves whether the present series of radio observations is really reliable.

Not long ago Ryle and his colleagues found the value 3.0 for the downward slope of the log N — log S line. Cynics say that they have now found 1.8 and next time it will be 1.5— fair enough as a joke, by the way, but not likely, as no tenable theory predicts 1.5. B. Y. Mills, the Australian radio astronomer, has also obtained about 1.8, but he thinks that there is a considerable margin of observational error—in fact, enough to bring the figure down to 1.5.

Ryle, however, firmly believes that his 1.8 cannot be reduced to 1.5 because of observational error, and maintains that the steady-state theory is therefore disproved. He admits mistakes in the past but thinks his present results must be taken seriously. As he said at the International Astronomical Union meeting in California in 1961, "Because we have been wrong in the past does not mean we are *necessarily* wrong now." *

* This willingness to admit when one is wrong is something scientists pride themselves on. Can anyone imagine, say, a politician, a bishop, or a salesman making a statement like this?

Nevertheless, there are radio astronomers who think Ryle is still wrong. One of them is R. Hanbury Brown of Manchester. I explained in Chapter 5 that an essential part of Ryle's thesis is that the radio sources he is counting have about the same power as the Cygnus A source. Hanbury Brown disputes this, and argues that the Cygnus A source is exceptional. He therefore considers that most of the sources are nearer than Ryle would have us believe. This would mean that the relative dearth of nearby sources (Figure 37) which Ryle observes is a rather local phenomenon, and does not necessarily apply to the whole universe. Hanbury Brown interprets Ryle's work in terms of a supercluster of galaxies to which I shall refer again in the next section. If Hanbury Brown turns out to be right, it will destroy Ryle's proof that the steady-state theory is wrong.

Bertrand Russell once said that when the experts disagree, the layman does well to keep an open mind. When it comes to radio telescopes, with their intricate electronics, I count as a layman, and I try to keep an open mind when radio astronomers disagree, which, as Damon Runyon used to say, is "more than no little." We shall have to await other surveys from radio telescopes at Sydney, Manchester, and elsewhere before we know certainly whether Ryle has exorcised the demons that have beset him in the past.

HOYLE HITS BACK

Right or wrong, the announcement of Ryle's results early in 1961 created a great stir not only among cosmologists but also in the scientific world in general. Indeed Ryle's work became headline news in the press, and journalists with a nose for scandal described the hard feelings which the report is said to have aroused among protagonists of the steady-state theory. Among other things, they wrote of the irritation of

Fred Hoyle that, although both he and Ryle work at Cambridge University, he knew nothing of the results until shortly before the official announcement, and so had no opportunity to prepare for this latest attack.

However this may be, Hoyle lost no time in putting up a determined resistance to the demolition of his theory. He is prepared to accept Ryle's observations as substantially correct, but argues that they are not inconsistent with a modified form of the steady-state theory which he has lately produced with the help of his pupil, V. Narlikar.

To understand Hoyle's modifications let us recall that galaxies show a considerable amount of clustering. The clusters may contain several thousand galaxies, and whereas a galaxy occupies a region 100,000 light-years across, a cluster may stretch across 10 million light-years. This fact is important when we ask ourselves what we mean by the homogeneity of the universe; because although all theories agree that (at a given time) the universe is homogeneous "on a sufficiently large scale," we are not quite certain what is meant by these five words. For example, some astronomers have suggested that clusters of galaxies can form superclusters. In this case a region of inhomogeneity (namely, that occupied by the supercluster) could be very large, perhaps 100 million light-years or more.

Hoyle's proposal for reconciling the steady-state theory with Ryle's work is essentially that we are inside a large supercluster (which I shall call a super-duper-cluster) extending to the limit of Ryle's observations. Within this, the perfect cosmological principle does not apply, and evolution can occur: in fact, Hoyle assumes that the chance of a galaxy becoming a radio source increases very markedly as it ages. By this means he is able to explain Ryle's picture (Figure 37), but according to him it refers simply to a "local irregularity" in the universe. Outside the cluster, there are other similar super-duper-clusters, and it is only when one considers the universe as a collection of *these* objects that it is in a steady and homogeneous condition of constant average density. In other words, the "average density" which according to the steady-state theory is everywhere the same in space and time has to be calculated as an average over a very much larger region than is normally taken.

Ryle was quick to point out an objection to this. If his observations are correct, the excess of distant sources extends out to a distance of 8,000 million light-years. Now the horizon of the steady-state model (beyond which it will never be possible for us to see) is only about 10,000 million light-years distant, so it is necessary to suppose that Hoyle's super-duper-cluster occupies nearly half the volume of the observable universe! If such large regions are not in a steady state, one may fairly ask whether the idea of a steady-state universe is a useful one.

It should in any case be pointed out that there is no good evidence for clustering on this scale. Whether there is clustering of clusters at all is an intricate question which has to be treated by complex statistical methods. So far, most astronomers believe that there is no cosmic unit larger than the ordinary cluster of galaxies. In the circumstances I think one can legitimately claim that the postulation of Hoyle's super-duper-clusters amounts to special pleading to save a theory in grave trouble.

Of course, if Hanbury Brown's criticism of Ryle's work should prove valid, the position would be different. It would mean that what Hoyle regards as the "local irregularity," instead of occupying a large fraction of the observable universe, would really be fairly local. In that case, astronomers would probably be more tolerant of an explanation of Ryle's work in terms of clustering.

I have described only the barest outline of Hoyle's theory

because the details are very complicated. Indeed, it seems that one of the great attractions of the steady-state model—its simplicity—is lost if Hoyle's modification is adopted. Bondi and Gold do not agree with Hoyle's latest work, and take the view that Ryle's observations, or his interpretation of them, are not yet reliable enough to disprove the steady-state theory in its original form.

THE AGES OF GALAXIES

According to the steady-state theory, galaxies are continually forming by condensation of the newly created matter. The universe therefore always contains many young galaxies. Further, the age-distribution of galaxies seen by any particular observer is affected by the fact that, since all galaxies partake in the expansion, the older galaxies tend to recede into the distance, and only recently formed ones are visible. This situation is different from that to be expected on the relativistic theory, according to which the galaxies were formed once for all in the distant past.

The age-distribution has recently been calculated by Ivan King of the University of Illinois, who has shown that according to the steady-state theory, half the galaxies seen by any observer should be younger than 2.3×10^9 years. King points out that the galaxies in our neighborhood seem to be much older than this, and the steady-state theory therefore appears to be in conflict with observation on this point.

Hoyle maintains that King's argument is inconclusive, mainly because our own galaxy and our near neighbors are not a typical sample. This looks like another rearguard action on the part of the steady-state theorists.

Work on the ages of galaxies is extremely important, not only because it may disprove the steady-state theory but also because of its possible effect on relativistic cosmology. The simple relativistic models described in Chapter 7 all give less than 10,000 million years for the interval that has elapsed since the start of the expansion. Because we know that the galaxies could not have existed at the great temperatures then prevailing, they must have formed subsequently. Therefore, if it can be shown that our Galaxy, or any other, is more than about 10,000 million years old, the simple models must be ruled out.

In Chapter 5 I mentioned the views of some astrophysicists that our Galaxy is older than 10,000 million years. Much more work must be done before these views are established, but if they ultimately prove to be correct, relativistic cosmologists will be forced to accept the λ-term in Einstein's equations, and to adopt a model such as Lemaître's, or one of the others referred to in Chapter 9.

14

conclusion

WHAT DO WE KNOW?

In this chapter I want to draw together the threads of this complicated subject. The reader, having been bombarded with theories, models, and disputed observations, may be excused for feeling confused and frustrated, and I feel keenly my duty to put the account in some sort of order for him. If in doing this I oversimplify, I ask to be forgiven.

What things in cosmology can we be reasonably sure of? First, that the universe expands, and that Hubble's law is at least roughly true. This means that the galaxies are rushing away from us, and the farther they are, the faster they move. The expansion is the most important feature of the subject, and is responsible for most of the properties that make our

conception of the universe so utterly different from the static
condition which has, until the last forty years, been an unquestioned cornerstone of scientific belief. It explains Olbers's
paradox, according to which we should, in a static universe,
be drowned in a flood of light from the distant stars. It predicts the curious optical properties of the world horizons,
described in Chapters 7 and 9, which, although not yet observed, must exist if our theories are correct. It also forces
those of us who do not accept the steady-state theory to specu-
late on the distant past and future of the universe, in the
knowledge that these must be completely different from its
present state.

The second fundamental point of agreement among
cosmologists is that on a large scale the universe presents, at
a given time, the same picture to all galactic observers. (The
steady-state theorists agree with this, but adopt an extended
version of it in which the phrase "at a given time" is deleted.)
This statement, which implies that our own position in the
universe is no more than an average one, is largely an article
of scientific faith, embodied in the cosmological principle.
There is no direct evidence for it, but none against, and no
scientist today would question it.

The picture which galactic observers see is an isotropic
distribution of galaxies showing the red shift. This isotropy
is an empirical observation and not a consequence of the
cosmological principle; for, as we saw when considering
models of a rotating universe, it is possible for a model to
satisfy the principle and yet be nonisotropic. Hence the
isotropy of our world picture is something which may not be
verified by more accurate observations if the universe really
does have a slight rotation.

According to the cosmological principle the average
density of matter in the universe should, at a given time, be
the same everywhere. We cannot verify this directly since we

do not see all points in the universe at the same time: as has been repeatedly pointed out, if we observe a region of the universe, say, 1,000 million light-years distant, we see it as it was 1,000 million years ago, and not as it is now. Nevertheless, over distances small enough for the light-travel time to be neglected, we can say that the average density is uniform.

A further point of general agreement is that about 99 percent of the universe is composed of hydrogen. The remaining 1 per cent is not part of the cosmological problem, because it consists of heavier elements generated in stars. The preponderance of hydrogen is, however, extremely important for us as it means that, unless there is creation such as is postulated in the steady-state theory, the universe must have experienced some process of rejuvenation within the last few billions of years; for otherwise it would consist almost entirely of heavier elements formed during the infinite past.

Finally, we know from the observed age of objects in our own Galaxy that the universe is at least 5,000 million years old and that any model with a time-scale of less than this must be ruled out. There is, however, no evidence concerning an upper age limit.

These are the parts of cosmology of which we feel most confident, and on which we all agree. Beyond this point, cosmologists at present fall into two camps—the relativistic and the steady-state, and most of our disagreements arise from this. It is time to summarize the cases for the two theories.

RELATIVITY *VERSUS* STEADY-STATE

I explained in the previous chapter that the observations are at present unfavorable to the steady-state theory. In the optical field, the work of Baum, and also that of his predecessors, suggest that the observed graph of red shift against distance is significantly different from that predicted by the steady-state model. In the radio field, Ryle finds a similar disparity between the observed number counts and those required by the theory. On the other hand, both sets of observations can be adequately accounted for by relativistic cosmology.

A number of objections, described in detail in the previous chapter, prevent the unqualified acceptance of these results and the consequent outright rejection of the steady-state theory. In my own view, the weight of evidence against the theory is now very heavy, and I shall be surprised if it survives for much longer, though the originators of the theory can be relied on to give it artificial respiration until the last possible moment.

Until definitive evidence is available, we can judge the theories only on aesthetic and philosophical grounds. From this point of view, the steady-state theorists can emphasize the simplicity of their model, and proclaim that it satisfies the perfect cosmological principle. They can also point out that the singular state which is so perplexing in the relativistic models is absent in their theory. The relativist, if he is fair, will admit all this, although he may, like Professor Dingle, find some rude words to say about the perfect cosmological principle.

What has the relativist to say in reply? It seems to me that his best argument is the following: If the steady-state model should turn out to be correct, we should have to give up not only relativistic cosmology but also general relativity itself, at least as a fundamental physical theory. The failure of relativistic ideas, particularly that of the conservation of energy, which is built into general relativity, would be too serious to be corrected by tinkering about with Einstein's field equations. This would mean, of course, that the general relativity explanation of local phenomena, like the orbits of the planets, is false too.

Now, the steady-state model, as explained in Chapter 12, is at present backed by no satisfactory theory. It cannot, for example, be used to predict the orbits of the planets. If general relativity is wrong, the steady-state theory cannot take its place, except as a phenomenological model of the universe on a large scale. We should be left with no correct theory of dynamics or gravitation. This is why the validation of the steady-state model would really overturn physics. In comparison, the other merits and demerits of the two approaches to cosmology seem comparatively trivial.

Of course, physics is not immune to revolutions, and we cannot argue from this that the steady-state model is wrong. What we can do with a clear conscience, however, is to reject the steady-state model as long as the observed evidence gives us the slightest reason for doing so.

THE FUTURE

In this final section I shall assume that the steady-state model will not survive further observations, and discuss some aspects of relativistic cosmology which seem to be important for the future.

First, I return to Baum's observations, and recall that they are consistent with a cycloidal model. When we work out the details of this model we find it rather unsatisfactory in two respects. First, the time since the start of the expansion is hardly more than 5,000 million years, which is uncomfortably short judged by the time scale of some processes going on in our Galaxy. Second, the average density of matter in the model is about 4×10^{-29} grams per cubic centimeter; this is 40 times greater than the observed average density, though, as was explained in Chapter 5, this latter is necessarily only a lower limit since it is computed on the basis of visible matter.

Neither of these objections is enough to dismiss the model. They do, however, make us cautious in accepting it too wholeheartedly. There is another reason, too, why it would be a mistake to jump to the conclusion that the cycloidal model is the correct one.

The interpretation of modern observations, such as those of Baum and Ryle, raises an important question to which an answer must be found, namely, the mode of evolution of galaxies. It seems that observers are now seeing so far into space that the most distant observed galaxies must be very much younger than local ones. They may, therefore, have different absolute brightnesses, and without a theory of how galaxies evolve we cannot allow for this. For example, it was pointed out in Chapter 13 that the Einstein–de Sitter model could be made to agree with Ryle's graph if a suitable rate of evolution were assumed. If we suppose different rates, other models too can be brought into agreement, and unless we know which rate is correct the observations do not determine a unique model. Similar difficulties arise in interpreting Baum's results, so we cannot say that these lead definitely to the cycloidal model.

To me this is regrettable because I have a preference for the cycloidal model, though I wish to see its singular states removed so that its history is a never-ending series of oscillations, as represented by Figure 24. Such a model has some of the advantages of the steady-state universe, without the very serious theoretical disadvantages. It has a reasonably simple mathematical form, and when averaged over sufficient periods of time, it can be regarded as being in a steady state. Moreover, it has no initial explosion, and no question arises of the creation of the universe in the finite past.

If the universe really is of cycloidal type, we shall have to consider carefully the questions raised by the second law of thermodynamics, referred to in Chapter 12. These will, I suspect, be answered when we find the mechanism which changes the contraction into expansion, and without which, of course, the oscillations cannot continue.

Whether or not the universe is cycloidal, cosmologists will be very relieved when the correct type of world model is known. At present we feel a certain indignity that we do not know for certain even the broad outlines of our subject, such as whether the expansion is slowing down, and whether space is curved. It is rather like being a geographer and not knowing whether the Earth is round or flat. With luck we shall not have to wait many more years now.

index